The Integration of Neuroscience and Psychiatry

The Integration of Neuroscience and Psychiatry

Edited by
HAROLD ALAN PINCUS, M.D.

Deputy Medical Director and Director, Office of Research, American Psychiatric Association; and Clinical Associate Professor in Psychiatry, Department of Psychiatry and Behavioral Sciences, George Washington University, Washington, D.C.

HERBERT PARDES, M.D.

Lawrence C. Kolb Professor and Chairman, Department of Psychiatry, College of Physicians and Surgeons, Columbia University, New York; Director, New York State Psychiatric Institute; and Director, Psychiatry Service, Columbia-Presbyterian Hospital, New York

AMERICAN PSYCHIATRIC PRESS, INC.
Washington, D.C.

Note: The authors have worked to ensure that all information in this book concerning drug dosages, schedules, and routes of administration is accurate at the time of publication and consistent with standards set by the U.S. Food and Drug Administration and the general medical community. As medical research and practice advance, however, therapeutic standards may change. For this reason and because human and mechanical errors sometimes occur, we recommend that readers follow the advice of a physician directly involved in their care or the care of a member of their family.

The paper used in this publication meets the minimum requirements of American National Standard for Information Sciences—Permanence of Paper for Printed Library Materials, ANSI Z39.48-1984.   ∞™

Library of Congress Cataloging in Publication Data

Main entry under title:

The Integration of neuroscience and psychiatry.

    (Clinical insights)
    "Derived from a symposium on neuroscience and psychiatry that was held at the 1984 Annual Meeting of the American Psychiatric Association"—Pref.
    Includes bibliographies.
    1. Neuropsychiatry—Congresses.   I. Pincus, Harold Alan, 1951- .
II. Pardes, Herbert, 1934-   .   III. American Psychiatric Association. Meeting (137th:1984: Los Angeles, Calif.)   IV. Series. [DNLM: 1. Biological Psychiatry—congresses.   2. Huntington Chorea—congresses.
3. Neurophysiology—congresses.   4. Neuropsychology—congresses.
5. Organic Mental Disorders—congresses.   WL 102 I575 1984]
RC327.I476   1985   616.89   85-11270
ISBN 0-88048-073-4 (soft)

Contents

Introduction   **viii**
Harold Alan Pincus, M.D.
Herbert Pardes, M.D.

1   Neuroscience and Psychiatry: An Overview   **1**
Herbert Pardes, M.D.
Harold Alan Pincus, M.D.

2   The Potential of Neuroscience Research for Clinical Psychiatry   **21**
Robert M. Post, M.D.

3   Toward the Integration of Neuroscience and Psychiatry   **39**
Steven M. Paul, M.D.

4   Huntington's Disease and the New Genetics: A Preview of the Future for Psychiatric Disorders   **53**
Nancy S. Wexler, Ph.D.
James F. Gusella, Ph.D.
P. Michael Conneally, Ph.D.
David Housman, Ph.D.

**5 Research at the Interface of
Psychiatry and Medicine**   77
Harold Alan Pincus, M.D.
David R. Rubinow, M.D.

Contributors

P. MICHAEL CONNEALLY, Ph.D.
*Professor, Department of Medical Genetics,
Indiana University Medical Center, Indianapolis*

JAMES F. GUSELLA, Ph.D.
*Assistant Professor, Neurology Service and Genetics Unit, Massachusetts
General Hospital; and Department of Genetics, Harvard Medical School*

DAVID HOUSMAN, Ph.D.
*Associate Professor, Center for Cancer Research,
Massachusetts Institute of Technology, Boston*

HERBERT PARDES, M.D.
*Lawrence C. Kolb Professor and Chairman, Department of Psychiatry, College
of Physicians and Surgeons, Columbia University; Director, New York State
Psychiatric Institute; and Director, Psychiatry Service,
Columbia-Presbyterian Hospital, New York*

STEVEN M. PAUL, M.D.
*Chief, Clinical Neuroscience Branch, Intramural Research Program,
National Institute of Mental Health, Bethesda, Maryland*

HAROLD ALAN PINCUS, M.D.
*Deputy Medical Director and Director, Office of Research, American
Psychiatric Association; and Clinical Associate Professor in Psychiatry,
Department of Psychiatry and Behavioral Sciences,
George Washington University, Washington, D.C.*

ROBERT M. POST, M.D.
*Chief, Biological Psychiatry Branch, Intramural Research Program,
National Institute of Mental Health, Bethesda, Maryland*

DAVID R. RUBINOW, M.D.
*Chief, Psychiatry Consultation-Liaison, National Institutes of Health; and
Chief, Unit on Peptide Studies, Biological Psychiatry Branch, Intramural
Research Program, National Institute of Mental Health, Bethesda, Maryland*

NANCY S. WEXLER, Ph.D.
President, Hereditary Disease Foundation, Santa Monica, California

Introduction

The neurosciences have exploded and the reverberations, already being felt in psychiatry, will intensify in the years ahead. Rapidly accumulating information about basic mechanisms of the brain is shedding new light on the biological underpinnings of behavior and cognition, and progress in elucidating the genetic component of psychiatric disorders is yielding, as a secondary product, an enriched understanding of environment's impact on biology and behavior.

As the explosion rumbles on, no one in the profession will be cushioned—neither those entering the field nor those who are well along in their careers and actively engaged in professional activities. Some of us argue that, historically, psychiatry has incorporated neuroscience; others anticipate that it will invigorate the profession; still others warn that too rapid and uncritical an acceptance of the new precepts will seriously threaten the field.

Unquestionably, a burst of knowledge can be both a threat and an opportunity. For the young student, it is likely that the expanding knowledge base of psychiatry represents challenge and opportunity. But what of the established clinician? Should the psychodynamically oriented psychiatrist be threatened? What does autoradiography have to do with ego mechanisms? How should the busy practitioner approach the mushrooming, often bewildering neuroscience literature? How will these advances affect the relationship between psychiatry and neurology? How will we as a profession understand the new information, integrate it into our current repertoire of skills, and use it to benefit ourselves and our patients?

This monograph is derived from a symposium on neuroscience and psychiatry that was held at the 1984 Annual Meeting of the American Psychiatric Association. Each of the contributors to this volume brings to neuroscience and psychiatry a diverse range of interests and expertise. All, however, share a conviction that neuroscience can be incorporated into psychiatry as a means of invigorating the field, contributing to sharpened therapeutic potency, and enabling it to respond more effectively to the needs of people with mental disorders.

In Chapter 1, Herbert Pardes and Harold Alan Pincus discuss selected aspects of neuroscience, highlighting its basic concepts, its developing tools and technologies, and principal questions and areas of interest for psychiatry. Then, citing developments in two key areas of psychiatric practice—diagnostic assessment and clinical treatment—the authors suggest how the field is moving on a convergent path with the neurosciences.

In Chapter 2, initial perspective on the interaction of basic science and clinical work is offered by Robert Post, a research psychiatrist well known for his work on biological aspects of affective illness, who is also acutely sensitive to the role of psychological issues in developing models of clinical disorders. Dr. Post describes how advances in brain imaging have enhanced our understanding of mental disorders and have contributed already to the development of treatment approaches. The clinical advances he discusses were developed on the basis of hypotheses generated from a knowledge of brain biology and are exemplified in his own work with carbamazepine in manic-depressive illness. He suggests how current work that is investigating facets of the H-P-A axis may promise to be equally significant in the future.

Steven Paul, a psychiatrist whose basic research on receptor physiology has gained wide recognition, elaborates in Chapter 3 on the relationship between basic science and advances in clinical care. Using the examples of dopamine, an established neurotransmitter, and cholecystokinin (CCK), a peptide recently determined to possess neuroactive properties, Dr. Paul describes in detail how knowledge of the role and mechanisms of these two substances can yield insights relevant to an understanding of psychiatric disorders.

The successful application of neuroscientific strategies to a neuropsychiatric syndrome is discussed by Nancy Wexler, James Gusella, P. Michael Conneally, and David Housman in Chapter 4. The authors describe their recent and dramatically successful application of molecular genetic techniques to the study of Huntington's disease. The discussion of the severe psychosocial aspects of Huntington's disease provides important insights into the relationship between neurological and psychiatric disorders. A key section of the chapter deals with the complex clinical and ethical issues that advances in neuroscience research are bringing to the practicing mental health professional.

In Chapter 5, Harold Alan Pincus and David Rubinow, a clinical researcher who administers the consultation-liaison service at the Clinical Center of the National Institutes of Health, describe trends in the evolving relationship between psychiatry and medicine in general and explore the potential for neuroscientific techniques to foster improved ties at this interface. The authors present a series of models depicting possible ways in which psychiatric and medical conditions can interact, comment on the mechanisms that underlie these relationships, and suggest research questions that can and should be addressed.

The scope of the monograph clearly is wide, and the issues, therefore, are reviewed and discussed selectively in an attempt to elucidate the advances and their implications. A brief volume cannot presume to provide psychiatrists and other mental health professionals more than a glimpse of developments in a rapidly expanding field. Nonetheless, we hope to convey the excitement and enthusiasm of this research and to encourage the optimism and motivation of clinicians and students who are willing to set out on an ongoing effort of continuing education in this area.

Harold Alan Pincus, M.D.
Herbert Pardes, M.D.

1

Neuroscience and Psychiatry: An Overview

Herbert Pardes, M.D.
Harold Alan Pincus, M.D.

1

Neuroscience and Psychiatry: An Overview

A recent *Vogue* magazine article identified the most exciting ongoing drama in medical science as "scientists' exploration of what really happens inside your head to produce your thoughts and emotions" (1). Twenty years ago, the scientists featured in such an article clearly would have been psychiatrists and clinical psychologists. This article, however, reported on the work of numerous other disciplines working on what Eric Kandel calls the most fascinating problem in contemporary biology: the neurobiology of thought processes (2).

The possibility that psychoanalytic psychiatry and psychology, on the one hand, and neurobiology and neurophysiology, on the other, may fuse to yield a newer and richer understanding of how we think and emote *is* as exciting a prospect as exists in health research today. The excitement is felt by students who are entering the neurosciences en masse, and it is seen in the exponential growth of new knowledge. The fact that this excitement is being described in publications ranging from a fashion magazine to a report prepared by the Congressional Office of Technology Assessment (3) as well as on prime time television (4) underscores its relevance to all psychiatrists.

But what is neuroscience? Does it threaten a psychiatric world composed of libidinal drives, ego defenses, and superego constraints? Will neurobiology intrude upon the practitioner's world, changing the nature of his or her practice? A qualified yes. Should the threat be avoided? An unequivocal no. For many clinicians, particularly those who trained in the 1940s, '50s, and '60s and had little exposure to research, this threatening infusion of new information may ultimately be in the service of adaptation. While the psychiatric practice of the 1990s will differ significantly from that of past decades, the changes will not nullify past experience. Psychiatrists who are sufficiently flexible to update their knowledge base continually and modify their practice accordingly will find that clinical acumen gained through years of working with psychiatric patients will be even more valuable when it is integrated with the information emerging from the neurosciences.

This chapter highlights key developments that are fostering, at an accelerating rate, the integration of neuroscience and clinical psychiatry. The first section of the chapter describes and defines neuroscience, discusses selected concepts and tools employed by scientists working in the field, and addresses broad questions of interest and opportunity. The second section reviews practices and procedures in clinical psychiatry that reflect the profession's increasing linkages with neuroscience and are contributing to increasing refinement, differentiation, and specificity in clinical care.

NEUROSCIENCE: EMERGENCE OF A FIELD

One difficulty in defining neuroscience is that it is a young discipline, a fact underscored by continuing uncertainty as to whether a singular or plural form of the noun best describes the collective of disciplines that comprise the field. Swazey (5) attributes the origin of the term to the multidisciplinary group of scientists who, under Frank O. Schmitt's leadership, established the Neurosciences Research Program in 1963 as a tool for effecting "a quantum step in an understanding of the mind." Kandel and Schwartz (2) designated publication of Sir John Eccles' *The Neurophysiological Basis of Mind*, in 1953, as marking the beginning of the modern era of neuroscience.

Regardless of its age or the term used to describe it, the exponential growth of both the field and its knowledge base is indisputable. In 1971, membership in the Society for Neuroscience was 250; 12 years later, aided by an estimated 200–300 percent expansion of graduate and postgraduate training programs in neuroscience, the Society counted more than 8,000 members, a rate of growth that recently prompted Floyd Bloom to remark that by the year 2000, every man, woman, and child in the United States will be a neuroscientist.

Who are the 8,000 currently certified neuroscientists? That question, too, requires a certain tolerance for ambiguity. Neuroscience transcends traditional disciplinary boundaries, a fact immediately apparent to the psychiatrist who peruses the literature of the field. Among the disciplines contributing diverse research perspectives, strategies, and tools to the study of brain and behavior are anatomy, physiology, physics, optics, electronics, genetics, biochemistry, pharmacology, ethology, psychology, neurology, psychiatry, neurosurgery, internal medicine, and information science.

Still, the question remains. What is neuroscience? As defined by the Congressional Office of Technology Assessment (OTA), neuroscience is "the term applied to research on how the nervous system works and how it is affected by disease" (3). A study group convened by the Institute of Medicine of the National Academy of Sciences (6) cites a somewhat more specific definition coined by the White House Office of Science and Technology Policy: "that body of research directed toward understanding the molecular, cellular, and intercellular processes in the central nervous system and the way in which those processes are integrated in CNS functional control systems, with emphasis on research relating CNS functions with behavior" (6).

In fact, the roots of contemporary neuroscience can be traced to more familiar terrain from which it is possible to identify core unifying principles of a diverse field that has direct and significant implications for the practice of psychiatry. The basic precepts of neuroscience stem from studies of the cell, a process summarized by Kandel and Schwartz (2). In the 19th century, Golgi developed histological techniques that permitted visualization of the neuron and all of its processes, work inspired and supported by the conceptual insights of Ramón y Cajal regarding the central role of the neuron to nervous system function. The foundations of electrophysiology, laid in the 19th century, had led, by the mid-1900s, to detailed descriptions of the mechanisms by which single nerve and muscle cells are able to propagate electrical impulses. The next gap in understanding nervous system function was synaptic; early studies in biochemical pharmacology have inexorably lead within the past 15 years to greater elucidation of the processes of neurotransmission and, today, to vastly expanded opportunities in neuroscience that are contributing significantly to the study and treatment of psychiatric and other illnesses.

Although this brief sketch of contemporary neuroscience offers little sense of the picture's overall complexity, it does pull together core concepts articulated in the OTA report:

1. that behavior, perception, and cognition are results of integrated actions of networks of nerve cells;
2. that understanding the anatomically precise and enormously complex activities of nerve cell networks requires explication of how such anatomic connections are made;
3. that the processes of cell-to-cell communication are fundamental to an understanding of nerve cell networks;
4. that electrical properties of individual cells are important in the transmission of impulses and in intercellular communications;
5. that the electrical properties of nerve and muscle cells are controlled by molecules on the surface of the cell (ion channels and specific receptors).

On the basis of these concepts, neuroscience research today is on the brink of discovering underlying neuronal functions that are key to understanding the brain mechanisms serving behavioral expression. It should hearten the clinical psychiatrist to know that the molecular and cellular emphasis that characterizes much of the field of neuroscience is tempered by a keen awareness of behavior; while the strategies and instruments of neuroscientists may differ from many of those currently used by psychiatrists, the ultimate goals of each discipline are complementary.

THE TOOLS AND STRATEGIES OF NEUROSCIENCE: A SAMPLING

The rapid accumulation of information about brain structure and function reflects both the inter- and multidisciplinary approaches inherent in neuroscience research as well as technological breakthroughs in such fields as molecular biology, physics, and computer science. The new technologies allow unprecedented access to and scrutiny of molecular and cellular processes, in vivo observation of brain function, and rapid analysis of vast quantities of data. The new technologies will permit definitive tests of many current hypotheses of mental illness and will lead to the development of more refined hypotheses based on new data.

An essential and highly productive part of the ongoing research occurs at the molecular level. At the synapses—the junctions between nerve cells where clinically useful treatments are known to exert their action—sensitive techniques permit the study of discrete molecular events involved in the biosynthesis, processing, storage, and release of neuroregulators. Enormous strides have been made in the identification of transmitter substances; in addition to the classical neurotransmitters that little more than a decade ago were believed to account for the bulk of synaptic transmission (7), increasing interest is focused on a rapidly expanding number of peptides. Approaches useful in identifying putative transmitter peptides include the isolation of molecules implicated in a particular physiological response; identification of endogenous compounds for receptors, a process that led to the discovery of endorphin; and the isolation and sequencing of genes that encode neuroactive peptides. Both immunological and chemical methods are being employed in this area. The ability to generate monoclonal antibodies directed against peptides and other transmitter candidates, for example, has meant that the distribution of these substances can be assessed quantitatively by radioimmunoassay and qualitatively by immunocytochemical techniques.

Across the synapse, techniques including high performance liquid chromatography, monoclonal antibodies, and cloning of genes that code for receptors are being used to identify new receptors, the macromolecules that constitute the initial element in the response of all cells to chemical stimuli. Although numerous reports have described changes in neurotransmitter receptors in disorders such as schizophrenia and affective illness, research is only beginning to analyze these changes in order to separate the impact of disease from the impact of treatment. Studies of receptors in vivo may help define some psychiatric conditions in terms of specific receptor dysfunction and thus further enhance specificity in clinical psychiatry.

Within the past decade, a variety of imaging techniques have been developed that allow the safe acquisition of regional, in vivo, biochemical information from the brain. This capacity reflects the key role in neuroscience of high energy physics, which has contributed the following apparatus: linear accelerators and cyclotrons and the capacity to synthesize radiopharmaceuticals; mathematical models that permit parameters of biochemical and physiological significance to be estimated from the data; and the engineering of detection systems that employ the concept of positron emission tomography (PET) to permit safe, nonintrusive in vivo monitoring of radiopharmaceuticals. Discovery by Sokoloff et al. in 1977 (8) of a means to measure regional brain metabolic activity on the basis of glucose utilization has had far-reaching effects on studies of in vivo brain function. Especially valuable to the study of psychiatric disease is the use of PET to provide quantitative measurements of local drug action, receptor pharmacology, and neurotransmitter metabolism. Strategies employing variations of Sokoloff's 2-deoxyglucose technique to study rates of local cerebral protein synthesis possess significant implications for understanding plasticity and maturation in the brain, hormonal influences, and relationships between learning and protein synthesis (9).

Other new technological procedures offer equally exciting opportunities for observing the brain. Nuclear magnetic resonance, NMR, translates measures of the distribution and chemical bonds of protons in hydrogen nuclei into three-dimensional images of tissue; in addition to providing anatomical information comparable to that available through computerized tomography (CT) scanning, NMR sheds light on the health of tissue (10). Also, the increasing sophistication of on-line microprocessors and mathematical techniques are making feasible the collection and analysis of simultaneous recordings of electrical activity of the brain through a process called BEAM, for brain electrical activity mapping (11). Insofar as such measures can be used to assess numerous aspects of brain function related to sensory, perceptual, and cognitive processes, they occupy the interface between cellular neurobiology and the behavioral or cognitive sciences.

AREAS OF INTEREST AND OPPORTUNITY

Collectively, these developments and others suggest the need for a broader view of research in mental disorders that will facilitate the integration of technological and substantive developments in neurotransmission, anatomy, physiology, and genetics into studies of the neural mechanisms important in mental illness. To address this point, a National Academy of Science task panel has identified several major research opportunities that promise to promote understanding of brain behavior and its relevance to major health problems (6). These include research on how the brain grows and maintains itself, research which builds on evidence regarding the differentiation of neuronal function, the plasticity and regenerative capacities of cells, and neuronal correlates of aging. A second area of opportunity involves studies of mechanisms with which the brain acquires, stores, and uses information at the molecular and cellular level as well as the level of behavior and social interaction. Third, exciting opportunities exist to explicate the brain's role in monitoring and regulating internal bodily processes; recent evidence suggests, for example, the previously unanticipated extent to which the brain serves as a mediator of behavioral phenomena upon the immune system. Research on the ways in which the brain expresses rhythms, drives, and emotions has resulted already in an ability to map neural pathways related to sexual behavior, aggression, and sleep patterns in animals and promises to contribute significantly to clinical understanding of these processes in humans. Finally, insofar as neuroscience continues to elucidate the basic mechanisms that underlie brain function, it will contribute significantly to the nature of clinical psychiatry and the quality of clinical care.

TRENDS IN CLINICAL PSYCHIATRY

It is understandable that many clinicians view developments in neuroscience as either academically interesting or vaguely threatening but of limited relevance to the practice of psychiatry. In this century, the profession has been subject to numerous shifts in orientation—for example, the acceptance of psychoanalysis in the first half of the century, the advent of pharmacologic treatments in the 1950s, and the reorientation to community-based patterns of care in the 1960s—that have had immediate, dramatic impact on the self-identity of psychiatry and the nature of psychiatric practice. In contrast, during the past decade of explosive growth in the neurosciences, it appears that no revolutionary shifts in the treatment of mental disorders have occurred. Upon closer examination, however, it can be seen that psychiatric practice has been influenced by trends that evolved over the past decade and that portend significant changes in the years ahead.

The first trend is increasing *differentiation* in psychiatry. This is typified by *DSM-III* (12). Research-based criteria for diagnosis have enhanced significantly the reliability of the system. While the reduced emphasis on clinical inference and increased emphasis on observable phenomena is perceived by some to present risks—for example, an atrophying of expertise in clinical assessment or the possibility of premature closure on diagnoses that may become outmoded as research progresses—the power of the approach is a feature critical both to researchers seeking homogeneous patient/subject populations and to clinicians providing services in a geographically mobile society.

A second trend is seen in the *refinement* of psychiatric data and the clinical procedures derived from it. The Epidemiologic Catchment Area (ECA) program (13), now underway at NIMH and participating research centers around the country, represents an ambitious attempt to sharpen the data upon which clinical care is based, the service delivery system is organized, reimbursement policy is set, preventive opportunities are sought, and clinical and research training needs are identified.

Differentiation and refinement contribute directly to a third evolving characteristic of psychiatry: increasing *specificity* in the provision of clinical treatments. Abundant evidence in diverse areas testifies to this trend—for example, the capacity to match specific short-term psychotherapeutic strategies to personality and developmental variables (14), and the identification of different spectrums of effects of monoamine oxidase inhibitors (15). Other developments discussed in this monograph also suggest an increasing specificity in clinical care.

These trends illustrate the strengthened scientific basis of both biological and psychosocial aspects of clinical psychiatry. In that respect, they mirror and complement the contributions of neuroscience to the field. The following sections review selected examples of more dramatic opportunities for interaction between neuroscience and clinical psychiatry, using two principle functions of the field—assessment and treatment—as a framework for discussion.

Advances in Psychiatric Assessment

While the phenomenological approach of *DSM-III* represents a substantial advance in diagnosis, neuroscience research also promises to have a dramatic impact on capacities in this area. Of particular interest, although not yet ready for broad clinical application, are a variety of laboratory diagnostic tests. The dexamethasone suppression test, DST (16), is based on evidence that indicates an abnormal cortisol response in many depressed patients to a challenge dose of the synthetic steroid dexamethasone. Presently of limited value in general medical settings, the DST appears to be useful in specialized psychiatric settings as a confirmatory test for endogenous or major depressive disorders (17). Similarly, the thyrotropin releasing hormone (TRH) test appears to have applications in highly specific situations (18). Urinary MHPG has been suggested as useful in selecting antidepressants (19). Although each of these tests requires further refinement and may yield to more precise measures, they do forecast what will emerge as a routine clinical procedure.

As noted previously, the advent of a variety of imaging techniques presents exciting opportunities for psychiatric research and clinical use. The EEG still is used clinically to assess organic mental disorders and epilepsy (20), but the newer technologies may relegate such discomforting procedures as pneumoencephalograms and arteriograms to texts on the history of medicine. Computerized tomography (CT) scanning is currently a routine procedure; as discussed by Post in this volume, research using CT scans suggests the presence of enlarged ventricles in schizophrenia, a finding that has been linked to the likelihood of reduced responsiveness to treatment.

Recent experience with nuclear magnetic resonance (NMR) promises that this newer technology may supplant the CT scan. NMR more precisely differentiates anatomical structure and appears to offer some assessment of brain function (21). With respect to measurement of function, however, NMR does not rival positron emission tomography, or PET scanning. Interest in this approach reflects the fact that all tissues that perform physical or chemical work exhibit a close relationship between energy metabolism and level of functional activity. Until recently, however, the variety of electrophysiological, anatomical, or histochemical methodologies available for examining cerebral functional activity were either so broad as to offer imprecise information or so detailed as to destroy the brain tissue under investigation or to introduce "sampling" errors because only a few out of billions of brain cells could be selected for study. In this context, the development by Sokoloff of a method to measure local rates of energy metabolism simultaneously in all components of the brain, and its application to photon detection technologies, constituted an advance in brain science comparable in significance to the introduction of chest roentgenograms 75 years earlier.

While clinical use of the PET scan has been most effective to date in locating epileptogenic foci, the procedure is evolving rapidly in sophistication and is being employed in numerous investigations of psychiatric disorder. Early reports of hypofrontality, or decreased function in frontal areas of the cortex in schizophrenia, await confirmation, and research focusing on manic depressive disease, Alzheimer's disease, and autism is ongoing. PET scans are also being used to determine anatomical areas which correlate with specific types of psychological functions. It has been found that when a subject is confronted with a verbal analogies test, greater activity is produced in the posterior regions of the left hemisphere. A spatial orienting task produces increased metabolic activity in the right hemisphere. Psychological and neuropsychological tests can be used with these PET scan techniques and findings to identify precise areas of deficit, thereby allowing considerable gains in the sophistication of diagnosis (22).

A number of developing techniques to subtype psychiatric disorders represent another encouraging trend in diagnosis and assessment. Recent demonstrations that panic disorders are qualitatively separable from other anxiety disorders are illustrative. For example, recent research employed administration of lactic acid to precipitate a panic episode in vulnerable subjects (23), and there is growing evidence regarding the efficacy of so-called antidepressants in suppressing panic attacks (24).

Buchsbaum and Maier (25) have suggested that the next step in the subtyping of disorders should entail a search for biological markers and a conceptualization of those markers as independent criteria rather than as dependent variables. Using markers, investigators could look for the associated symptoms of patients with the marker and possibly introduce different syndromes or disease entities than those currently recognized. This strategy may hold particular promise for research on schizophrenia; rather than looking at the syndrome in its entirety, researchers could focus efforts on discrete components of the disorder.

Conceptual and technological advances in molecular genetics promise to contribute directly to the search for markers and to subsequent implications for the management and treatment of illness. The possibilities in this area are seen clearly in Chapter 4 of this monograph. Because Huntington's disease typically does not manifest symptoms until patients reach mid-adult life, genetically vulnerable persons are hampered severely in decisions regarding marriage, child-rearing, career choices, and so forth. The recent finding of a marker by Gusella et al. (26) will allow potentially vulnerable people to be tested and possibly given information regarding their risk. Further, the capacity for prenatal diagnosis exists.

Because psychiatric disorders in families seem to segregate in a manner consistent with multiple-threshold, polygenic models rather than with major locus transmission (27), identification of specific markers is somewhat more complex. Goldin and Gershon suggest, however, that this may not preclude finding major locus traits that correlate with disease susceptibility. With the combination of attempts to develop subtypes and the accumulation of information from genetic studies (28), the possibility exists that subtypes of major psychiatric disorders will be differentiated on the basis of these genetic approaches.

Still another emerging approach to assessment is found in the appraisal of neurotransmitter system function. For example, with respect to Alzheimer's disease, a disorder in which a genetic factor is operative, new techniques have elucidated some of the neurophysiological and biochemical defects characteristic of the disease. Of particular interest is the finding of selective degeneration of specific acetylcholine-releasing neurons in the basal forebrain (29). These cholinergic neurons innervate widely the cerebral cortex and related structures and apparently play a major role in cognitive functions, particularly memory. These findings are contributing to diagnostic capacity and, ultimately, will enhance the specificity of treatments. A behavioral complement to this development is seen in recent work by Weingartner et al. (30) to design specific psychological tests that will differentiate the memory dysfunction associated with Alzheimer's disease from other diagnostic entities. They have found that with patients with Alzheimer's, the loss of capacity to connect new information to their contextual network of memories produces a memory dysfunction distinguishable from that associated with Parkinson's disease or depression. Thus, promising developments for the diagnosis of this neuropsychiatric disorder are emanating from both biological and psychological perspectives.

This selective review indicates the variety of strategies and technologies now under development that will enrich clinical psychiatry's capacities in this area. A psychiatric diagnostic assessment in the future will be more comprehensive and more precise with regard to prognosis and treatment. Not insignificantly, it also will be more highly regarded within the medical profession and peripherally by those involved with reimbursement and policy.

Advances in Psychiatric Treatment

Advances in diagnosis and assessment of disorders not only enable greater specificity in the choice of treatment but also permit more productive refinement and assessment of treatments; these advances contribute, in turn, to further gains in classification, including elucidation of the relative roles of biological and psychosocial factors in the nature and course of disorders. Recent developments in the treatment of affective illnesses illustrate this synergy. Major depression is among the most common of psychiatric disorders and accounts for much of the time of psychiatrists. The introduction of psychopharmacologic agents has made the treatment of depression a setting in which the interplay of biology and psychology is prominent. Abundant evidence supports the effectiveness of diverse psychotherapies, pharmacotherapies, and electroconvulsive therapy in the treatment of depression. The work of DiMascio et al. (31), showing that combinations of treatments offered the most effective means of response to some depressions, now serves as a prototype of the value of integrating biological and psychotherapeutic modalities in psychiatric care.

Further, advances in the subtyping of affective disorders have shown that treatments are differentially useful with discrete subgroups of patients and for discrete subsets of symptoms within a given patient. The tricyclics are most effective in treating unipolar illness; lithium is more effective in bipolar forms of the illness and appears to help approximately 70 percent of patients with manic-depressive disease. Recent studies have further elaborated the difference in efficacy. While lithium is effective in preventing recurrences of mania, tricyclics are more effective in preventing recurrences of depression. However, tricyclics may precipitate manic episodes in some patients who have an underlying bipolar illness. This underscores the need for thorough assessment and careful consideration in the selection of treatment modalities (32).

The choice of treatment for depression in the elderly is particularly important given the high incidence of the illness in this age group, the likelihood of polydrug use for a variety of medical conditions, and the difficulty in distinguishing symptoms from co-occurrent disorders or masking syndromes such as Alzheimer's disease. Also, the development of many "second generation" drugs has expanded considerably the choice of agents available to the clinician. Attention to specific side-effects and previous patient history with a given drug are the most useful criteria for drug choice. As we learn more about the way the elderly use and respond to drugs, it is becoming apparent that the course of treatment should consist of initial low doses with incremental increases (33).

Benzodiazepines have proven useful both as a treatment for anxiety and as a substitute for sedative and hypnotic drugs. Because their use is complicated by addiction and withdrawal syndromes, Shader and Greenblatt (34) encourage the use of nonpharmacologic methods in treating nonincapacitating and situational forms of anxiety. When anxiety is severe and prolonged, adjunctive treatment is appropriate, with antidepressants used for phobic and panic states, and anxiolytics (for example, benzodiazepines) for generalized anxiety disorder and a mixture of anxiety and depression. While benzodiazepines currently are preferred among anxiolytics, newer nonbenzodiazepine compounds may provide increased safety.

Basic research at the molecular and cellular levels, applications of imaging technologies to studies of neural pathways and receptor systems, and increasing differentiation among psychiatric syndromes, are making possible a scientific fast-track between bench and bedside that clearly will yield drugs of increased potency and diminished risks. Nonetheless, the likelihood that neuroscience ultimately will develop a pharmacologic silver bullet for disorders such as schizophrenia or affective illness is fanciful thinking. The far greater likelihood is that, like mental retardation, the severe mental disorders will be shown to be composed of multiple deficits, each of which requires specific treatments. Unlike Huntington's disease, it is probable that the schizophrenias and depressions will reflect varying degrees of genetic contribution. Research conducted to elucidate the relative contributions of genetic and environmental factors will be tied closely to elaborations of instances in which biological and behavioral interventions are most effective and, in turn, appropriate. This is exemplified in evolving perceptions of treatment needs in hyperkinetic behavior/attention deficit disorder, in which pharmacologic treatments are viewed as clinically insufficient and the search for behavioral complements is under way. Similarly, in schizophrenia, attention to the psychological environment of the family now is seen as crucial to both understanding and treating the syndrome (35).

Given the increased reliance upon both psychological and pharmacological therapies, and the possibility of the use of different forms of psychotherapies for specific disorders, which is now being evaluated in the NIMH Psychotherapy of Depression Collaborative Project (36), the need for multiple skills on the part of the clinician will increase dramatically. More exact ways of prognosticating which treatments will be most effective for which conditions will be developed and refined, as will procedures for monitoring patients to determine both needed modifications and optimal duration of treatment. The importance of the latter is seen in recent evidence that depressions last longer than had been recognized previously and that they must be monitored carefully to determine when treatment can be tapered or terminated safely.

CONCLUSIONS

Change breeds anxiety. A scholarly endeavor, however, ideally should embrace and absorb new information. Thus, the opportunities and strengthened capacities being brought by the neurosciences to the practice of psychiatry are welcome. For those who view psychiatry as a central part of medicine, the development of more refined, differentiated, and specific procedures in assessment and treatment represents a worthy challenge. Mastery first requires recognition that the challenge exists. The fundamental aspect of psychiatry's identity and its greatest contribution is the bridging of behavior and biology. The neurosciences have captured the imagination and attention of society, and psychiatry has the potential and the responsibility to be on the leading edge of this "most exciting ongoing drama in medical science."

References

1. Switzer E: Brainwork. Vogue, November 1983, pp 468ff

2. Kandel ER, Schwartz JH: Principles of Neural Science. New York, Elsevier North Holland, 1981

3. Office of Technology Assessment: Impacts of Neuroscience: Background Paper. Washington, DC, US Congress, Office of Technology Assessment, OTA-BP-BA-24, 1984

4. Public Broadcasting System: The Brain. Eight part television series aired fall 1984

5. Swazey JP: Forging a neuroscience community: a brief history of the Neurosciences Research Program, in The Neurosciences: Paths of Discovery. Edited by Worden FG, Swazey JP, Adelman G. Cambridge, The MIT Press, 1975

6. Committee on Science, Engineering, and Public Policy: Report of the Research Briefing Panel on Neuroscience. Washington, DC, National Academy Press, 1983

7. Snyder S: Biological Aspects of Mental Disorder. New York, Oxford University Press, 1980

8. Sokoloff L, Reivich M, Kennedy C, et al.: The [^{14}C]Deoxyglucose

method for the measurement of local cerebral glucose utilization: theory, procedure, and normal values in the conscious and anesthetized albino rat. J Neurochem 28:897–916, 1977

9. Kennedy C, Suda S, Smith CB, et al.: Changes in protein synthesis underlying functional plasticity in immature monkey visual system. Proc Natl Acad Sci USA 78:3950–3953, 1981

10. Ritman EL, Kinsey JH, Robb RA, et al.: Three-dimensional imaging of heart, lungs, and circulation. Science 210:273–280, 1980

11. Morihisa JM, Duffy FH, Wyatt RJ: Brain electrical activity mapping (BEAM) in schizophrenic patients. Arch Gen Psychiatry 30:719–728, 1983

12. American Psychiatric Association: Diagnostic and Statistical Manual of Mental Disorders, 3rd ed. Washington, DC, American Psychiatric Association, 1980

13. Regier DA, Myers JK, Kramer M, et al.: The NIMH epidemiologic catchment area program. Arch Gen Psychiatry 41:934–941, 1984

14. Burke JD, White HS, Havens LL: Which short-term therapy: matching patient and method. Arch Gen Psychiatry 36:177–186, 1979

15. Murphy DL: Substrate-selective monoamine oxidases: inhibitor, tissue, species, and function differences. Biochem Pharmacol 27:1889–1893, 1978

16. Carroll BJ: Anxiety/depression: current management and future directions. Biological markers and treatment response. J Clin Psychiatry 44:30–40, 1983

17. Hirschfeld RMA, Koslow SH, Kupfer DJ: The clinical utility of the dexamethasone suppression test in psychiatry. JAMA 250:2172–2175, 1983

18. Loosen PJ, Prange AJ Jr: Thyrotropin releasing hormone (TRH): a useful tool for psychoneuroendocrine investigation. Psychoneuroendocrinology 5:63–80, 1980

19. Schildkraut JJ, Orsulak PJ, Schatzberg AF, et al.: Toward a biochemical classification of depressive disorders, I: differences in urinary MHPG and other catecholamine metabolites in clinically defined subtypes of depressions. Arch Gen Psychiatry 35:1427–1433, 1978

20. Fenton GW: The electroencephalogram in psychiatry: clinical and research applications. Psychiatric Developments 2:53–75, 1984

21. Rollo FD: New imaging modalities: positron emission tomography and nuclear magnetic resonance. Med Instrum 15:53–54, 1982

22. Buchsbaum MS, Ingvar DH, Kessler R, et al.: Cerebral glucography with positron tomography: use in normal subjects and in patients with schizophrenia. Arch Gen Psychiatry 39:251–259, 1982

23. Rifkin A, Klein DF, Dillon D, et al.: Blockade by imipramine or desipramine of panic induced by sodium lactate. Am J Psychiatry 15:676–677, 1981

24. Zitrin CM, Klein DF, Woerner MG, et al.: Treatment of phobias, I: comparison of imipramine, hydrochloride, and placebo. Arch Gen Psychiatry 40:125–138, 1983

25. Buchsbaum MS, Maier RJ: Psychopathology: biological approaches. Annu Rev Psychol 34:410–430, 1983

26. Gusella JF, Wexler NS, Conneally PM, et al.: A polymorphic DNA marker genetically linked to Huntington's disease. Nature 306:5940, 234–238, 1983

27. Goldin ER, Gershon EJ: Association and lineage studies of genetic marker loci in major psychiatric disorders. Psychiatric Developments 1:387–418, 1983

28. Nadi NS, Nurnberg J, Gershon EJ: Muscarinic cholinergic receptors on skin fibroblasts in familial affective disorder. N Engl J Med 311:225–231, 1984

29. Coyle JT, Price DL, Delong MR: Alzheimer's disease: a disorder of critical cholinergic innervation. Science 219:1184–1190, 1983

30. Weingartner H, Grafman J, Boutell W, et al.: Forms of memory failure. Science 221:380–382, 1983

31. DiMascio A, Weissman MM, Prujoff BA, et al.: Differential symptom reduction by drugs and psychotherapy in acute depression. Arch Gen Psychiatry 36:1450–1456, 1979

32. National Institutes of Health, Office of Medical Applications of Research: Mood disorders: pharmacologic prevention of recurrences. Consensus Development Conferences Consensus Statement, vol 5, no. 4. Bethesda, National Institutes of Health, 1984

33. Busse E, Simpson D: Depression and antidepressants and the elderly. J Clin Psychiatry 44:35–39, 1983

34. Shader RI, Greenblatt DJ: Some current treatment options for symptoms of anxiety. J Clin Psychiatry 44:21–30, 1983

35. Falloon IRH, Boyd JL, McGill CW, et al.: Family management in the prevention of exacerbations of schizophrenia: a controlled study. N Engl J Med 306:1437–1440, 1982

36. Elkin I, Parloff M, Hadley S, et al.: The NIMH treatment of depression collaborative research program: background and research plan. Arch Gen Psychiatry 42:305–316, 1985

2

The Potential of
Neuroscience Research for
Clinical Psychiatry

Robert M. Post, M.D.

2

The Potential of Neuroscience Research for Clinical Psychiatry

Sigmund Freud, a neurologist, postulated that we would eventually find a neuropathology of the psychiatric disorders and that abnormalities of behavior might be traceable to alterations in neural connectivity and responsivity. His predictions about the biochemistry of behavior were particularly insightful, given the absence of knowledge of the detailed structure of the nervous system at the time. In this chapter, I selectively review progress made toward an understanding of behavioral dysfunction on a neural and molecular level. While a neurobiology of psychodynamics has not been well elucidated, the state of current progress suggests that this may well be possible in the near future. This chapter will review examples on a neuroanatomical, physiological, neuropsychological, functional, biochemical, and pharmacological basis, of the practical applications and implications for the future of psychiatry.

BRAIN IMAGING

Rapid advances have been made in the brain imaging techniques. Little more than a decade ago, we had only the relatively insensitive skull x-ray, which could pick up pathological calcifications, an abnormal sella turcica, or gross fractures of the skull, but could convey little information about internal aspects of the brain. Modern computerized axial tomography (CAT) scan techniques revolutionized our access to brain structures. We can now visualize the gross structure of the brain and delineate the volume of the fluid-filled ventricular spaces deep within.

This ability has made possible the recent finding that many patients with schizophrenia have large ventricular brain ratios—an increased size of ventricular volume compared to brain volume (1). While this has been thought to be a relatively static structural change, recent data (2) suggest the possibility that alterations in the hormonal milieu of the central nervous system (CNS) may be capable of changing the ventricular brain ratio (VBR) along with brain function. When patients are treated with high doses of corticosteroids or adrenocorticotropin hormone (ACTH), an increased VBR and evidence of brain atrophy can emerge. With cessation of this treatment, the findings are reversible. Similarly, Kellner et al. (2) reported that patients with high urinary-free cortisol may have larger ventricular brain ratios when in a depressed state. These findings have been replicated recently by Reus et al. (3), who reported that ventricles were markedly increased in size in depressed patients who had cortisol hypersecretion, as documented by escape from dexamethasone suppression. Rubinow et al. (4) reported that patients with increases in excretion of urinary-free cortisol also showed more impairments in cognitive function, as measured on the Halstead Categories Test of the Halstead-Reitan Battery. These findings have been replicated by Reus et al., who demonstrated a relationship between VBR, cortisol hypersecretion, and degree of cognitive defect. The causal links in these relationships remain to be delineated, but they raise the possibility that subjective and objective measures of cognitive impairment in depressed patients may have both structural and endocrinological concomitants.

Finer anatomical resolution is promised by techniques of nuclear magnetic resonance (NMR). Our research team at the National Institute of Mental Health (NIMH) has scanned our first depressed patient and has observed a remarkable delineation of the grey and white matter and fine structures of the brain. This technique promises to enable specific confirmation of recently reported findings based on autopsy specimens. For example, Dr. Timothy Crow (5) reported that, in contrast to affectively ill patients, patients with schizophrenia show a reduction in the ratio of size of left-to-right para-hippocampal gyruses. NMR techniques, which provide a resolution and a picture almost equivalent to that of brain slices, should soon be able to confirm or deny this finding. However, even with the high degree of resolution made possible by NMR, the ability to assess brain function, as opposed to structure, appears to be relatively limited with this technology.

In contrast, there has been recent progress in computer interfacing of older neurophysiological techniques, such as EEG and averaged evoked potential. With these brain electrical activity mapping (BEAM) techniques, topographic maps of the surface electrical activity of the brain can be delineated. Buchsbaum et al. (6) demonstrated that, in some instances, mapping by this technique can be compared with PET scan techniques used in the measurement of glucose activity. In unpublished data, Putnam and colleagues have demonstrated that patients with multiple personality disorder have topographies that are significantly different, whereas a normal person, attempting to simulate different personalities, does not. BEAM and EEG techniques, reported on by Morihisa et al. (7), also hold potential for more refined neuropsychiatric assessment and diagnosis.

The pioneering study by Ingvar (8) documented alterations in patterns of cerebral blood flow across a number of psychiatric conditions. He was the first to suggest that hypofrontality may be a concomitant of schizophrenia. His findings recently have been extended by Weinberger et al. (9), who reported that dorsal-frontal blood flow was markedly reduced in schizophrenics when they were engaged in a paired-associate learning task with which they had difficulty, but not when they were performing a continuous performance task. These findings, indicating task-specific alterations in regional blood flow, are considerably important in their own right, but are especially noteworthy because of their emphasis on the ability of modern techniques to assess alterations in underlying brain function during behaviorally relevant tasks, and tasks that are, in fact, capable of uncovering differences among different diagnostic groups.

This potential is even more dramatically revealed by recent PET scan studies of Phelps (10). He measured glucose utilization, which is a measure of brain activity, with position emission tomography. He found that different areas of the brain showed increased glucose utilization depending on whether subjects were looking, listening, thinking, remembering, or working. These activities produced increases in occipital cortex, angular gyrus, frontal cortex, temporal lobe, and motor cortex, respectively. Moreover, the remarkable sensitivity of this technique for assessing alterations in thinking patterns was demonstrated by his finding that the type of processing involved in listening to music altered the laterality of the increased glucose utilization. When naive subjects merely listened to music, their right cortices were more active than their left; however, when highly trained professionals processed the music in a more analytical manner, their left cortices were more activated. Thus, the techniques of positron emission tomography have the demonstrated capability of revealing the anatomy and physiology of thought processes.

Phelps also found alterations in cerebral metabolic rates depending on mood state. For example, depression was associated with decreased glucose utilization in many brain areas. An earlier study had indicated that decreased left temporal-frontal glucose utilization was particularly striking in bipolar, but not unipolar, depressed patients. These findings have been paralleled by those of Buchsbaum et al (6), who found relative hypofrontality in depressed patients, particularly based on an apparent increase in glucose utilization in posterior or occipital regions rather than merely frontal decrements. In addition, DeLisi and associates, in an unpublished study, have observed that in depressed patients decreased left and right temporal glucose utilization improves following recovery. Employment of appropriate neuropsychological tasks during testing should further elucidate important biological alterations in a variety of neuropsychiatric diagnoses.

NEW PHARMACOLOGIC TREATMENTS: CARBAMAZEPINE AND CLONIDINE

Although these imaging techniques hold great promise, one can ask what advances based on neuroscience progress already have been made in clinical psychiatry. Limbic system mechanisms have long been implicated in the modulation of emotional function (11–13). Based on this finding, our research group at NIMH began a search for a pharmacological agent that might have a central role in dampening pathological activity in limbic system structures. We were struck by the efficiency of carbamazepine in the treatment of complex partial seizures that were thought to arise from temporal lobe and limbic substrates. The anticonvulsant effects of carbamazepine were documented both in the clinical setting and in animal models of limbic epilepsy, such as those derived from amygdala kindling. Kindled seizures are those which gradually develop following repetitive stimulation of the brain with currents that initially are subthreshold.

This empirical evidence led to our initiation of the first double-blind clinical trials of carbamazepine in both depression and mania. Previously, only uncontrolled clinical trials had been performed in Japan. Our work has led to the development of a new treatment for manic-depressive illness, particularly for those who are inadequately responsive to lithium carbonate (14). We observed that carbamazepine has an acute antimanic efficacy with a time course similar to that achieved by neuroleptic treatment. However, carbamazepine does not act by blocking dopamine receptors and, thus, does not convey the risk of acute parkinsonism side effects or those of longer-term, more problematic instances of tardive dyskinesia. In addition to its acute antimanic efficacy, we have observed, in an unpublished study, antidepressant effects in 20 of the first 37 patients (54 percent), with robust responses in 13 patients (35 percent). With longer-term administration, we have documented that for patients who are lithium-nonresponders carbamazepine may be an alternative treatment for prevention of both manic and depressive relapses. In a study of seven patients followed for an average of 1.7 years, we observed a decreased frequency of both manic and depressive episodes from 16.4 ± 5.7 in the year prior to carbamazepine administration to 5.7 ± 2.4 in the year of carbamazepine treatment (15).

While the theoretical rationale for the use of carbamazepine in manic-depressive illness remains to be explicitly tested and confirmed (14, 16), the initial data in our laboratory and in others throughout the world indicate that a substantial proportion (approximately 65 percent) of patients who do not respond to lithium may be treated successfully with this anticonvulsant. We have initiated a series of studies designed to assess whether other anticonvulsants that are less effective on limbic system mechanisms are also less effective in the treatment of manic-depressive illness. Our initial case study of the first patient to be crossed over to two other anticonvulsants is consistent with this formulation. This patient responded dramatically to carbamazepine on two different occasions, while two administrations of placebos and treatment with phenytoin and valproic acid were without effect (17).

In another area, a more direct pharmacological treatment application has been derived from basic neuroscience research. Clonidine, an agent often used for the treatment of hypertension, inhibits the firing of the locus coeruleus. Upon the basis of this finding, Gold et al. (18) investigated and found that clonidine is useful in the treatment of opiate withdrawal syndromes, and they have developed the first nonnarcotic treatment of opiate dependence and addiction. These findings were based on observations, made in the animal laboratory using neurophysiological techniques, that clonidine markedly decreased the firing of the noradrenergic locus coeruleus. Opiate abstinence in animals was associated with a marked increase in firing. It was thus reasoned that by decreasing this mechanism, opiate abstinence syndromes might be blocked. This hypothesis was confirmed in a series of studies indicating that clonidine administration dramatically reversed not only anxiety but also many of the other withdrawal symptoms of acute opiate abstinence. Uhde et al. (19) also found that clonidine administration blocked the development of opiate abstinence syndromes, and that it was associated with antianxiety effects in anxious-depressed patients as well as in patients with panic anxiety disorders (20). These data potentially implicate noradrenergic mechanisms in a variety of anxiety syndromes of different etiologies.

NORADRENERGIC FUNCTION: ENVIRONMENTAL CONTEXT AND CONDITIONING

Alterations in noradrenergic mechanisms also have been postulated to underlie the mood disturbances of manic and depressive illness. In longitudinal studies, patients consistently demonstrate increases in 3–methoxy, 4–hydroxy-phenylglycol (MHPG) or norepinephrine in the urine, blood, or spinal fluid during the manic as opposed to the depressed phase of the illness, even though studies of groups of patients who were compared to normal volunteers are less consistent. The noradrenergic locus coeruleus contains approximately 10,000 neurons in the rat and in man, as many as 50,000–100,000 neurons. This one small nucleus and neurotransmitter system has diffuse projections and widespread effects throughout the brain. Thus, it is ideally suited for a brainstem arousal mechanism.

Recent studies have indicated that alterations in the firing of the locus coeruleus can be associated with a specific "meaning" for an animal. Segal and Bloom (21) found that locus coeruleus activity could potentiate either increases or decreases in the firing of neurons in the hippocampus, depending on whether the associative cues had been previously linked to a positive or negative reward. Thus, the signal function of locus coeruleus firing can be modulated by environmental (psychosocial) determinants and events. This is further documented in studies of learned helplessness that indicate that the ability to cope with a given noxious stimulus can determine the change in brain norepinephrine. If an animal is subjected to shock from which it can escape by appropriate mechanisms, it will not evince depletion in brain or plasma norepinephrine. In contrast, a yoked control animal, receiving a shock of identical intensity and duration, will show depletions in norepinephrine when its behavior is inconsequential to the removal of the painful stimulus. Thus, the psychosocial state of the animal, based on past experience, can affect ongoing brain mechanisms and biochemistry. Similarly, these biochemical reactions can be conditioned. Merely placing an animal back in the environment in which it was originally shocked is sufficient to reproduce some of the original biochemical depletions (22–25). These studies pave the way for ultimately demonstrating a neuroscientific base for understanding psychodynamics and its interrelationship with psychopharmacology.

NEUROPEPTIDES AND BEHAVIOR: CORTICOTROPIN-RELEASING FACTOR (CRF) AND SOMATOSTATIN

While careful analysis of noradrenergic mechanisms in relation to behavior holds great promise for understanding psychobiological interactions in neuropsychiatrically ill patients, it should be remembered that the brain contains approximately 10 billion neurons, only a few of which contain norepinephrine. The recent neuroscience revolution has elucidated more than 30 putative peptide neurotransmitter candidates in the brain. These may play a major role in the activation or inhibition of a substantial number of the 10 billion neurons. Almost all of these putative neurotransmitters are measurable in the cerebrospinal fluid (CSF), providing one initial and preliminary, if global, means of assessing neurotransmitter peptide function in man.

What is the role of peptide neurotransmitters in relation to neural regulation and behavior? This question becomes increasingly interesting in light of the finding that many peptides can coexist within individual neurons and at times coexist with classical neurotransmitters. For example, Swanson (26) has described remarkable findings about the CRF neuron. In addition to containing CRF, it contains vasopressin, angiotensin, enkephalin, neurotensin, neuropeptide y, and substance-p. Thus, a total of seven neuropeptides can be found within an individual cell. Swanson reported that the manifestation of these peptidergic properties would change depending on the hormonal milieu. For example, following adrenalectomy, there were increases in CRF, vasopressin, and angiotensin, all of which enhance secretion of ACTH.

Various stresses appear to stimulate CRF and ACTH secretion, suggesting that this peptidergic system may play a complex role in behavior, adaptation, and homeostasis, with major consequences for survival and reproduction of the species. Ovine CRF was isolated, identified, and sequenced by Vale et al. in 1981 (27). Hundreds of tons of ovine hypothalamus were required in order to complete this localization. Bloom (28) now has circumvented this process and has identified brain-specific peptides, using techniques of recombinant DNA and molecular biology. In the three years since CRF was identified and sequenced, it has already yielded a clinically valuable result. Gold et al. (29) found in our laboratory that depressed patients showed blunted ACTH responses to intravenous administration of ovine CRF. This suggests that CRF hyposecretion may occur in depression, with feedback regulation by the associated cortisol hypersecretion producing the blunted ACTH response to CRF. The locus of the defect in Cushing's disease appears to be different; these patients also showed marked cortisol hypersecretion, but, in contrast to the depressed patients, they showed markedly exacerbated, rather than blunted, ACTH response to CRF.

Thus, in only three years, the clinical applicability of the neuroscience advances in sequencing CRF are already apparent. They form the basis of a differential diagnostic test for depression and Cushing's disease, two pathological processes that are often confused because in both are found cortisol hypersecretion and attendant behavioral and depressive symptoms. The treatment implications for the two syndromes are very different, however. Thus, this test may be of increasing clinical importance in distinguishing between them. Moreover, the findings suggest that the pathophysiological locus of the defect is different in depression and in Cushing's disease, with normal feedback regulation occurring at the pituitary level in depression but perhaps with pathology occurring at the hypothalamic locus or above. These findings provide a further dissection of the locus of cortisol hypersecretion in depression, which has been documented in thousands of patients in hundreds of studies across multiple investigative groups in many countries.

A final example illustrates the potential of the new "peptide-ology" for psychiatry in perhaps an even more compelling fashion. Somatostatin appears to be a peptide that is altered in CSF or brain of patients in a variety of neuropsychiatric illnesses. It is decreased both in brain and CSF of patients with Alzheimer's disease. The defects are most apparent in the temporal cortex, but many areas of the cortex are involved. In contrast, patients with Huntington's chorea have increases in somatostatin in the striatum. Crow (5) recently reported that type 2 or negative-symptom schizophrenic patients have selective defects in somatostatin in the hippocampus. CSF somatostatin has been reported to be low in parkinsonian patients and low in patients with active multiple sclerosis, but normal in patients in remission.

These findings are of particular interest in relation to those of Rubinow et al. (4). In our laboratory, they found that somatostatin spinal fluid was low in patients during depressed phases but increased toward normal in patients in manic and improved phases. Thus, there appears to be a state-related decrease in somatostatin in depression. These findings are paralleled by those of Gerner and Yamada (30), Agren and Lundqvist (31), Black et al. (32), Bissette et al. (32), and Doran et al. (unpublished), all of whom found reductions in somatostatin in CSF of depressed patients.

Carbamazepine significantly decreases somatostatin in CSF. It also induces escape from dexamethasone suppression and increases excretion of urinary-free cortisol in those with normal basal levels of excretion (34). These data suggest the possibility that the reductions in somatostatin might be associated with cortisol hypersecretion. This suggestion has been confirmed by Doran et al. in an unpublished study. They found, in both depressed patients and schizophrenics, that those who escaped from dexamethasone suppression had significantly lower levels of CSF somatostatin. This is another example of the clinical application of a finding that only recently has been elucidated on a basic neuroscience level.

Heisler et al. (35) reported that somatostatin inhibited CRF-induced ACTH secretion. Less than two years later, evidence of this potential mechanism (decreased somatostatin) has been found in patients and could account for cortisol hypersecretion in depression and other neuropsychiatric syndromes. Interestingly, cortisol hypersecretion and escape from dexamethasone suppression have been reported in Alzheimer's disease and anorexia nervosa, two syndromes that have been reported to have low CSF somatostatin. Somatostatin administered to animals decreases total and rapid eye movement sleep duration. It is then of considerable interest that in one study, even though somatostatin levels were low in depressed patients in general, those with higher levels of somatostatin had decreased total sleep (4).

Although no effective means of pharmacologically manipulating somatostatin currently exist, ongoing studies may begin to elucidate potential strategies for affecting this increasingly important substance. For example, it is unclear by what mechanism carbamazepine decreases CSF somatostatin; does the decrease relate more to the anticonvulsant effects or to the other psychotropic effects of the drug? It has been demonstrated recently that depleting somatostatin with cysteamine, or inhibiting somatostatin function with antibodies, exerts anticonvulsant effects against amygdala-kindled seizures (36). Thus, there is indirect evidence that it is the anticonvulsant effects of carbamazepine that accounts for the decrease in somatostatin. Moreover, the induction of amygdala-kindled seizures yields a long-lasting (two months) increase in brain somatostatin (37), a finding which suggests that seizures, as well as anticonvulsive mechanisms, may impinge on this system. Altering somatostatin's biosynthetic pathways or its degradative processes may ultimately be clinically productive in treating seizure disorders or the somatostatin defects of Alzheimer's disease.

Recent findings in molecular biology also raise the possibility of more direct manipulation of this system. Palmiter et al. (38) demonstrated that transfer of the growth hormone gene into mouse eggs results in the production of enlarged mice because of an increased production of the growth hormone. However, Lowe et al. (39) also transferred the somatostatin gene directly from one mammal to another, but no change in growth was evident. Nonetheless, the finding that such a transfer is possible raises the interesting possibility that genetic manipulation may ultimately be important in the treatment of some neuropsychiatric syndromes, such as Alzheimer's disease.

A final possibility for manipulating somatostatin is through somatostatin transplants and brain implants. David Jacobowitz (personal communication, 1983) has demonstrated that somatostatin taken from neonatal mice will survive in implants to the cerebral cortex of adult mice. Although somatostatin terminals did not grow out of the transplant, the neurons apparently survived intact for long periods of time. Two brain implants of somatostatin have already been performed in an attempt to increase dopaminergic function in Parkinson's disease, and the early findings suggest the possibility that this strategy may have an application in neuropsychiatric disorders such as Alzheimer's dementia, a disease in which depletions in somatostatin may be relevant to the pathophysiological processes of the illness. Thus, implantation of somatostatin and manipulation of somatostatin metabolism directly or indirectly may be important in the treatment of Alzheimer's dementia and related neuropsychiatric syndromes in the future.

CONCLUSIONS

I have tried to illustrate through a variety of examples the tremendous clinical impact that neuroscience advances have made on the clinical diagnosis and treatment of many neuropsychiatric illnesses. Clonidine and carbamazepine are clinically useful treatments for opiate withdrawal and manic-depressive illness, respectively. Their introduction into clinical practice has been based largely on principles of modern neuroscience. Recently discovered neuropeptides appear to be intimately linked to the modulation of behavior and stress responsivity. The pathophysiological locus of cortisol hypersecretion in depression has been further elucidated with CRF tests. Studies of somatostatin promise to yield important insights not only for depression but also for Alzheimer's disease. In depression, the low levels of somatostatin (which inhibits ACTH) may also help explain increased cortisol secretion. A variety of imaging techniques for elucidating the fine structure, electrophysiology, and glucose utilization of the brain promise to yield equally rich rewards in the diagnosis, understanding, and treatment of psychiatric syndromes in the future.

Thus, the revolution in neurobiology has already had a substantial clinical impact and promises to drastically alter psychiatric practice in the future. One can imagine an increasingly sophisticated neurobiology that will be able to deal with the complexities of brain/behavioral interactions and, ultimately, with individual psychodynamics. I look beyond the promise implied by my title to the future acceptance of the statement, "Psychiatry is a neuroscience."

References

1. Weinberger DR, Wyatt RJ: Cerebral ventricular size: a biological marker for subtyping chronic schizophrenia, in Biological Markers in Psychiatry and Neurology. Edited by Usdin E, Hanin I. New York, Pergamon Press, 1982

2. Kellner CH, Rubinow DR, Gold PW, et al.: Relationship of cortisol hypersecretion to brain CT scan alterations in depressed patients. Psychiatry Res 8:191–197, 1963

3. Reus VI, Deicken R, Miner C, et al.: Correlates of marked nonsuppression. New Research Abstracts #NR29. Paper presented at the 137th Annual Meeting of the American Psychiatric Association, Los Angeles, May 5-11, 1984

4. Rubinow DR, Gold PW, Post RM, et al.: Somatostatin in affective illness. Arch Gen Psychiatry 40:403–412, 1983

5. Crow TJ: Disturbances in the temporal lobe. Abstract #20C. Paper presented at the 137th Annual Meeting of the American Psychiatric Association, Los Angeles, May 5-11, 1984

6. Buchsbaum MS, DeLisi LE, Holcomb HH, et al.: Anteroposterior gradients in cerebral glucose use in schizophrenia and affective disorders. Arch Gen Psychiatry 47:1159–1166, 1984

7. Morihisa JM, Duffy FH, Wyatt RJ: Brain electrical activity mapping (BEAM) in schizophrenic patients. Arch Gen Psychiatry 40:719-728, 1983

8. Ingvar DH: "Hyperfrontal" distribution of the cerebral grey matter flow in resting wakefulness: on the functional anatomy of the conscious state. Acta Neurol Scand 60:12-25, 1979

9. Weinberger DR, Berman KF, Zec RF: Schizophrenia dementia. Abstract #88E. Paper presented at the 137th Annual Meeting of the American Psychiatric Association, Los Angeles, May 5-11, 1984

10. Phelps ME: The biochemical basis of cerebral function and its investigation in humans with positron CT. Paper presented at the 137th Annual Meeting of the American Psychiatric Association, Los Angeles, May 5-11, 1984

11. Papez JW: A proposed mechanism of emotion. Arch Neurol Psychiatry 38:725-743, 1937

12. MacLean PD: The limbic system and its hippocampal formation: studies in animals and their possible application to man. J Neurosurg 11:29-44, 1954

13. Gloor P, Olivier A, Quesney LF, et al.: The role of the limbic system in experiential phenomena of temporal lob epilepsy. Ann Neurol 12: 129-144, 1982

14. Post RM, Ballenger JC, Uhde TW, et al.: Efficacy of carbamazepine in manic-depressive illness: implications for underlying mechanisms, in Neurobiology of Mood Disorders. Edited by Post RM, Ballenger JC. Baltimore, Williams and Wilkins, 1984

15. Post RM, Uhde TW, Ballenger JC, et al.: Prophylactic efficacy of carbamazepine in manic-depressive illness. Am J Psychiatry 140: 1602-1604, 1983

16. Post RM: Are the psychotropic effects of carbamazepine in manic-depressive illness mediated through the limbic system? J Psychiatr Res (in press)

17. Post RM, Uhde TW, Berrettini W: Selective response to the anticonvulsant carbamazepine in manic-depressive illness: a case study. J Clin Psychopharmacol 4:178–185, 1984

18. Gold MS, Redmond DE Jr, Kleber HD: Clonidine in opiate withdrawal. Lancet 1:929, 1978

19. Uhde TW, Redmond DE Jr, Kleber HD: Clonidine suppresses the opioid abstinence syndrome without clonidine-withdrawal symptoms: a blind inpatient study. Psychiatry Res 2:37–47, 1980

20. Uhde TW, Siever LJ, Post RM: Clonidine: acute challenge and clinical trial paradigms for the investigation and treatment of anxiety disorders, affective illness, and pain syndromes, in Neurobiology of Mood Disorders. Edited by Post RM, Ballenger JC. Baltimore, Williams and Wilkins, 1984

21. Segal M, Bloom FE: The action of norepinephrine in the rat hippocampus, IV: the effects of locus coeruleus stimulation on evoked hippocampal unit activity. Brain Res 107:513–525, 1976

22. Herman JP, Guillonneau D, Dantzer R, et al.: Differential effects of inescapable footshocks and of stimulation previously paired with inescapable footshocks on dopamine turnover in cortical and limbic areas of the rat. Life Sci 30:2207–2214, 1982

23. Cassens G, Kuruc A, Roffman M, et al.: Alterations in brain norepinephrine metabolism and behavior induced by environmental stimuli previously paired with inescapable shock. Behav Brain Res 2:387–407, 1981

24. Anisman H: Vulnerability to depression: contribution of stress, in Neurobiology of Mood Disorders. Edited by Post RM, Ballenger JC. Baltimore, Williams and Wilkins, 1984

25. Vogel WH: Animal models of depression: the model of learned helplessness, in Symposium on Special Aspects of Psychopharmacology. Edited by Ackenheil M, Matussek N. Paris, Expansion Scientifique Francaise, 1983

26. Swanson LW: Role of norepinephrine in the brain from lab to man:

anatomy. Paper presented at the 137th Annual Meeting of the American Psychiatric Association, Los Angeles, May 5-11, 1984

27. Vale W, Speiss J, Rivier C, et al.: Characterization of a 41-residue ovine hypothalamic peptide that stimulates secretion of corticotropin and beta-endorphin. Science 213:1394-1397, 1981

28. Bloom FE: Molecular approaches to the characterization of neuronal function. Marjorie Guthrie Lecture in Genetics, National Institutes of Health, Bethesda, MD, April 19, 1984

29. Gold PW, Chrousos GP, Kellner CK, et al.: Psychiatric implications of basic and clinical studies with corticotropin releasing factor. Am J Psychiatry 14:619-627, 1984

30. Gerner RH, Yamada T: Altered neuropeptide concentrations in CSF of psychiatric patients. Brain Res 238:298-302, 1982

31. Agren H, Lundqvist G: Low levels of somatostatin in human CSF mark depressive episodes. Psychoneuroendocrinology 9:233-248, 1984

32. Black PM, Ballantine HT, Carr DB, et al.: Beta-endorphin and somatostatin concentrations in the cerebrospinal fluid of patients with depressive disorder. Paper presented at the Proceedings of the Society of Biology and Psychiatry, Los Angeles, May 2-6, 1984

33. Bissette G, Walleus H, Widerlov E, et al.: Reductions of cerebrospinal fluid concentrations of somatostatin-like immunoreactivity (SRIF-LI) in dementia, major depression, and schizophrenia. Society for Neuroscience Abstracts 10:137, 1984

34. Rubinow DR, Post RM, Gold PW, et al.: The relationship between cortisol and clinical phenomenology of affective illness, in Neurobiology of Mood Disorders. Edited by Post RM, Ballenger JC. Baltimore, Williams and Wilkins, 1984.

35. Heisler S, Reisine TC, Hook VYH, et al.: Somatostatin inhibits multireceptor stimulation of cyclic AMP formation and adrenocorticotropin secretion in mouse pituitary tumor cells. Proc Natl Acad Sci USA 79:6502-6506, 1982

36. Higuchi T, Sikand GS, Kato N, et al.: Profound suppression of kindled seizures by cysteamine: possible role of somatostatin to kindled seizures. Brain Res 288:359–362, 1983

37. Kato N, Higuchi T, Friesen HG, et al.: Changes of immunoreactive somatostatin and beta-endorphin content in rat brain after amygdala kindling. Life Sci 32:2415–2422, 1983

38. Palmiter RD, Norstedt G, Gelinas RE, et al.: Metallothionein: human GH fusion genes stimulate growth of mice. Science 222:809–814, 1983

39. Lowe M, Goodman RH, Brinster R, et al.: Expression of a metallothionein somatostatin fusion gene in transgenic mice. Abstracts of the American Federation for Clinical Research 32(2):549a, 1984

3

Toward the Integration of Neuroscience and Psychiatry

Steven M. Paul, M.D.

3

Toward the Integration of Neuroscience and Psychiatry

This chapter will convey a sense of how the tools of basic neuroscience research have been used to bridge the gap between our understanding of the fundamentals of nervous system activity and the various clinical disorders that are of interest to the practicing psychiatrist. Because neuroscience research has expanded exponentially in the last 10 or 15 years, we can only speculate about what areas will prove fruitful in the years to come. I have chosen several examples of recent research that illustrate our emerging capacity to use neuroscience research in the clinical setting.

Ten or 15 years ago, only a few neurochemicals in the brain had been identified as neurotransmitters. Subsequent clinical research has attempted to link excesses or deficiencies of these substances to various neuropsychiatric conditions. With the development of gas chromatographic/mass spectrometric and radioimmunoassay methods in the mid-1970s, our ability to detect substances in the brain that function as neurotransmitters has greatly increased the degree of sophistication by which biological studies of neuropsychiatric diseases can be conducted. Most psychiatrists are familiar with the classical neurotransmitters: acetylcholine, dopamine, noradrenaline, norepinephrine, epinephrine, serotonin, and gammaaminobutyric acid (GABA), to name a few. The identification and characterization of these compounds, which represent, perhaps, less than five percent of the brain's neurotransmitters, have already been important in understanding higher nervous system functions and the pathophysiology of various neuropsychiatric disorders. For example, there is neuropathological evidence that many of the memory and cognitive defects observed in patients with Alzheimer's disease derive from a deficit in the functioning of specific cholinergic (acetylcholine-containing) neurons that project to critical areas of the cerebral cortex (1). This hypothesis is given further support by the effects of drugs that either increase or block cholinergic neuronal action. Dopamine (DA), previously linked to the motor deficiencies of Parkinson's disease, which are caused by the degeneration of neurons that comprise the nigrostriatal DA system, is suspected of being a prime mediator of psychotic symptomatology in schizophrenic patients. Moreover, recent clinical data have related changes in dopamine "turnover," as reflected in changes in plasma DA metabolites, to both a reduction and an exacerbation of schizophrenic symptoms (2). Other biogenic amine neurotransmitters, such as norepinephrine, epinephrine, and serotonin, have been implicated in the pathogenesis of the affective disorders with indirect evidence that antidepressant drugs work by altering—most likely by increasing—the functional activity of these neurotransmitters in the brain (3). There is also evidence that most, if not all, anti-anxiety agents work by enhancing the activity of the brain's major inhibitory neurotransmitter, gamma-aminobutyric acid (GABA). It has never been proposed that this neurotransmitter is involved in the pathophysiology of "fear" or "anxiety" (4). This chapter will attempt to highlight the clinical significance of these exciting discoveries, which evolved from basic neuroscience research.

THE CHEMISTRY OF THE BRAIN

In a sense, the real explosion in the neurosciences came a few years ago with the discovery of many previously unknown neuropeptides that are present in the brain. These peptides serve as neurotransmitters in some cases and, in others, as neuromodulators. Neurotransmitters transmit selective and discrete biochemical signals at the synapse, while neuromodulators alter the sensitivity or efficacy of the signals mediated by such neurotransmitters. The endogenous opiate peptides or endorphins, were discovered because of their ability to bind to opiate receptors and to mimic the effects of morphine. At least three genes produce virtually all of the opiate peptides in the central nervous system (5). It has been postulated that this family of peptides has a variety of functions, subserve mood and analgesia, and are involved in the organism's response to various forms of "stress." Substance-P, another peptide present in the brain and spinal cord, is thought to be a mediator of some forms of pain. With the discovery of each new neuropeptide or neuromodulator, new hypothetical relationships between the substance and physiological or clinical phenomena emerge. The "programming" of basic research toward an understanding of complex clinical phenomena is inevitable; however, one can argue that basic research in neurobiology should also be independent of any preconceived clinical context. If one examines the history of major discoveries in other branches of medicine, it is obvious that a great deal of basic research is required before meaningful clinical findings emerge.

GUT PEPTIDES IN THE BRAIN

Cholecystokinin (CCK) is a gastrointestinal peptide that potently affects gall bladder function and pancreatic enzyme secretion. First described in the gut, CCK is also present in high quantities in the brain. Cholecystokinin has 33 amino acids, and the critical amino acid sequence includes the last eight amino acids (octapeptide) at the C terminus. The sulphate group on the tyrosine in the seventh position is an absolute requirement for biological activity in the gastrointestinal tract and for many of its central actions as well. Curiously, there are large quantities of CCK in many brain regions—the cerebral cortex has a very high concentration of CCK, and, at present, CCK may be the most quantitatively important peptide in the central nervous system. Although CCK levels are highest in the cerebral cortex, there are also relatively high concentrations of the peptide in the basal ganglia and limbic system.

Most of the CCK that is stored in the cerebral cortex is stored in cell bodies that project to the corpus striatum (basal ganglia). By visualizing CCK receptors through the use of light microscopic autoradiography, it is apparent that the striatum is a very important target for CCK's actions. A receptor is the membrane site (usually a protein complex) of action of neurotransmitters and drugs. Thus, once a neurotransmitter is released into the synaptic cleft, it binds to a specific recognition site (the receptor) somewhere on the postsynaptic membrane, and subsequently sets up a series of biochemical events that result in a physiological event, such as increased or decreased neuronal excitability.

Experiments in our laboratory, employing the neurotoxin kainic acid, indicate that the intrinsic cell bodies in the striatum contain most of the CCK receptors. Interestingly, patients with Huntington's disease have a marked deficit in the number of these receptors. In Huntington's disease there is a degeneration of cell bodies, which contain a variety of receptors, including CCK receptors. The loss of CCK receptors in Huntington's disease is limited to the basal ganglia and is correlated both with neuronal cell loss and with other neuropathological changes. It is possible that the loss of CCK receptors or the loss of other neurotransmitter receptors may contribute to the signs and symptoms of this disorder (6). CCK receptors have also been localized to various regions in the forebrain, including the cingulate gyrus and the nucleus accumbens of the septum, two brain regions that have been implicated in the pathophysiology of schizophrenia.

DOPAMINE AND CHOLECYSTOKININ: THE CONCEPT OF COTRANSMITTERS

In the last few years, numerous exceptions to Dale's Law, which postulates the existence of only one neurotransmitter per neuron, have become apparent. Classical neurotransmitters, such as dopamine, and peptides, such as cholecystokinin, have been demonstrated to coexist in the same neuron. Most of the brain's dopamine-containing neurons originate in the brainstem and midbrain and project rostrally to the corpus striatum and other regions of the forebrain such as the nucleus accumbens. There are four known dopamine pathways in the central nervous system, including the DA pathway from the substantia nigra to the striatum, and the ventral tegmental pathway of the mesencephalon, which projects to many of the limbic (forebrain) areas such as the nucleus accumbens and the central nucleus of the amygdala. In a classic study, Hökfelt et al. (7) demonstrated, by using immunocyto-chemical techniques, that CCK and DA coexist in only a subpopulation of DA neurons, namely those in the ventral tegmental pathway. By using antibodies directed against the dopamine-synthesizing enzyme tyrosine hydroxylase and another antibody against CCK itself, these investigators demonstrated specific immunochemical staining for both substances in the same neuronal perikaryon. By using retrograde tracing techniques, they were able to document the exact projection of these coexisting CCK/DA neurons.

What does coexistence of two or more neurotransmitters mean from the standpoint of function? In the rat, CCK coexists in dopamine neurons only in the mesolimbic pathway—the ventral tegmental pathway to the nucleus accumbens, the area of the brain that has been implicated, for example, in schizophrenia. CCK does not exist in DA neurons of the substantia nigra that project to the striatum. Consequently, a number of experiments have been carried out to try and elucidate what may be the physiological significance of this CCK/DA coexistence.

In an extension of their original work, Skirboll et al. (8) found that CCK, when injected intravenously in animals, markedly potentiates dopamine's ability to presynaptically inhibit the firing rate of substantia nigra neurons. Crawley et al. (9) have recently shown that CCK injected directly in the brain alters postsynaptic DA activity as well. Moreover, the effects of CCK on DA activity appear to be confined to those areas where the peptide and amine coexist. In other words, CCK appears to modulate dopamine neurotransmission, and this effect is confined to the ventral tegmental DA pathway. For example, an injection of low concentrations of CCK (less than 200 picograms) into the target area of the ventral tegmental DA pathway—the nucleus accumbens—will result in a marked potentiation of dopamine's ability to increase locomotor activity. In contrast, when CCK is injected into the head of the caudate nucleus (only a few millimeters from the nucleus accumbens) there is no evidence of the potentiation of DA activity (9). Thus, the potentiation of DA activity by CCK occurs only in an anatomical region where both are co-localized. If one imagines the many possible ways (given the number of coexisting neurotransmitters already identified) that transmitters and co-transmitters can modulate one another, it is apparent that the coexistence "phenomenon" may represent an important physiological mechanism for regulation of neurotransmitter function.

This research has clinical implications as well. It has been postulated, for example, that if one could administer a CCK antagonist to a schizophrenic patient, it may result in a reduction in psychotic symptoms, if the symptoms are caused by an "excess" of dopamine. By modulating the co-transmitter, one could also modulate the primary transmitter. Furthermore, these studies suggest that the anatomic and neurochemical differences in brain dopamine pathways have important functional consequences. For example, differences between the ventral tegmental dopamine pathway and the nigrostriatal pathway may be important in predicting the side-effect profile as well as the therapeutic efficacy of antipsychotic drugs.

DOPAMINE AND SCHIZOPHRENIA

Studies by Creese et al. (10) and Seeman et al. (11) have shown that the relative potencies of neuroleptic drugs, such as chlorpromazine, thioridazine, and haloperidol, in decreasing psychotic symptoms in schizophrenic patients, are directly proportional to their potencies at binding to postsynaptic dopamine receptors. Moreover, there is evidence that the side-effect profile (sedation, orthostatic hypotension, and so forth) of neuroleptic drugs can be predicated by the interaction of these drugs in vitro with various other neurotransmitter receptors, such as the muscarinic-cholinergic, histaminergic, and alpha adrenergic receptors (12).

These studies suggest that the blockade of dopamine receptors is somehow involved in the antipsychotic actions of neuroleptic drugs. Furthermore, it is possible that the dopamine receptor itself might somehow be altered in schizophrenia, but this is still an area of active debate. Lee et al. (13) reported an increased number of dopamine receptors, which were labeled using radioactively labeled neuroleptics, in postmortem brain specimens from schizophrenic patients compared to those from controls. Others, however, have attributed these changes to the effects of neuroleptic treatment per se (14), although Seeman obtained a small subset of samples from schizophrenic patients who presumably had never received any antipsychotics (15). Studies of neurotransmitter receptors in postmortem brain tissue are complicated by a number of variables, including postmortem interval (autolysis time) and the effects of the normal aging process (most postmortem samples are obtained from elderly patients).

Fortunately, it may be possible in the near future to directly measure and quantify dopamine receptors in living human brain. Wagner et al. (16) were the first to demonstrate and visualize dopamine receptors in man using positron emission tomography (PET). These investigators were able to radioactively tag the potent neuroleptic agent spiperone with a positron-emitting isotope (^{11}C). Since spiperone has been shown to be a potent and relatively selective ligand for dopamine receptors in biochemical experiments and can label dopamine receptors using in vivo techniques in animals, it was reasonable to assume that the ^{11}C–spiperone would be useful for visualizing DA receptors in man. The PET studies demonstrated a relatively discrete localization of the ^{11}C–spiperone in areas of the brain known to be enriched in DA receptors (16). In particular, the basal ganglia was an area of intense localization of radioactivity. Although still in its infancy, this method theoretically could be used to quantify DA receptors in schizophrenic patients early in their treatment, perhaps before there are neuroleptic-induced changes in DA receptor number.

Several very interesting findings have already emerged from these studies. First, a significant decrease in the number of DA receptors occurs during aging, particularly in men. Thus, studies that examine DA receptors using PET must control for the age of the patient. The finding that DA receptor function decreases with increasing age is interesting, since Parkinson's disease is generally found in older people and thus may occur, at least in part, as a result of the combined effects of a normal decline in postsynaptic DA function and a degeneration of presynaptic DA afferents to the basal ganglia. The PET method for measuring DA receptors probably will soon be applied to the question of whether there is an increased number of DA receptors in various brain regions of schizophrenic patients. This method should also be applicable to a number of other neurotransmitter receptors.

DOPAMINE AND SCHIZOPHRENIA: NEW EVIDENCE

The evidence that DA receptors are somehow involved in the antipsychotic actions of neuroleptics is rather convincing. Receptor binding studies have shown good correlations between neuroleptic potency and the relative affinities of neuroleptics for DA receptors in both rat and human brain (15). However, clinically the antipsychotic effects of neuroleptics usually require several weeks to develop, whereas their acute effects in blocking DA receptors occur immediately. The relationship between receptor blockade and the time "lag" required for antipsychotic activity recently has been examined using electrophysiological techniques. These studies were first carried out by Chiodo et al. (17) and have been extended by White and Wang (18). In animals, the activity of dopamine neurons in midbrain is increased during acute treatment with antipsychotic drugs. During chronic administration, however, neuroleptics reduce the spontaneous firing rate of dopamine neurons in both the substantia nigra (A9) and the ventral tegmentum (A10). Interestingly, recent work suggests that those neuroleptics that are associated with a low incidence of extrapyramidal side effects (EPS) fail to alter dopamine neurons in A9 but reduce the spontaneous firing rate in A10. Conversely, those neuroleptics associated with a high incidence of EPS are all effective in reducing the spontaneous firing rate of A9. These data suggest that the differential sensitivity of dopamine neurons to neuroleptics may account for the clinical differences, observed among neuroleptics, in their propensity to produce extrapyramidal side effects (18).

More important, the decrease in dopamine neuronal activity following chronic neuroleptic administration may account for the delay in the time course of antipsychotic activity observed in schizophrenic patients. Thus, acute receptor blockade leads to the development of a "functional" decrease in dopamine-neuronal activity during chronic administration. In fact, it appears that, initially, neuroleptics increase the activity of dopamine neurons by activating a compensatory feedback loop that somehow "senses" the postsynaptic blockade of dopamine receptors. Apparently, the firing rate increases to the point where the neuron is unable to generate an action potential, resulting in a phenomenon called depolarization inactivation. The neurons are firing so quickly as a result of DA receptor blockade that their functional activity is actually decreased. This effect occurs in A10 (ventral tegmental dopamine pathway) with virtually all neuroleptics tested so far, but occurs in A9 (nigrostriatal pathway) only with those that are most often associated with the development of EPS. Therefore, it has been suggested that the antipsychotic actions of neuroleptics result primarily from an action on dopamine neurons in the ventral tegmental pathway. The exact biochemical mechanisms responsible for the ability of neuroleptics to discriminate among the various dopamine pathways is unknown. However, it appears that neuroleptics selectively reduce the "presynaptic" release of dopamine during chronic administration and that this effect may underlie their antipsychotic properties. Clinical support for a neuroleptic-induced decrease in presynaptic dopamine activity has recently been reported at our laboratory at NIMH (2).

The evidence that dopamine is involved in the pathophysiology of schizophrenia has been derived almost exclusively from experiments with animals. With the exception of the studies of DA receptors in postmortem brain, there has been little direct support for the DA hypothesis from studies on schizophrenic patients themselves. Recently, Pickar et al. (2) measured the principal dopamine metabolite in plasma, homovanillic acid (HVA), in a group of schizophrenic patients and in controls. Since previous work had shown that about 30 to 40 percent of plasma HVA is derived from the central nervous system, these investigators reasoned that changes in plasma HVA, produced by neuroleptic treatment, might be indicative of the therapeutic activity of these drugs. When schizophrenic patients were taken off their neuroleptics for four weeks, plasma HVA levels increased compared to the levels when patients were receiving neuroleptics and compared to healthy controls. These findings are consistent with an increase in dopaminergic function or "turnover" in unmedicated schizophrenic patients. When the same patients were treated with a potent phenothiazine, fluphenazine, a time-dependent decrease in plasma HVA was observed. Plasma HVA levels were significantly reduced (compared to baseline) by the third, fourth, and fifth weeks of treatment. Virtually all patients demonstrated a reduction in plasma HVA during neuroleptic administration. When the clinical effects of neuroleptics in individual patients were compared to the patients' plasma HVA levels, there was an excellent correlation between the decrement in plasma HVA and the decrease in psychotic symptoms. Moreover, when all plasma HVA determinations (made at any time in the study) were correlated with the blind psychosis ratings of both nurses and doctors, made at a similar point in time, there was a fairly robust correlation (2).

These results suggest that monitoring plasma HVA may represent a measure of presynaptic dopamine "function" and that changes in plasma HVA correlate with psychosis (and improvement in psychosis) in schizophrenic patients, both during neuroleptic treatment and withdrawal. However, even if the changes in plasma HVA observed in our patients reflect changes in brain HVA, our results do not necessarily suggest that schizophrenia is caused by a simple elevation in dopamine "turnover." I think most investigators would agree that, at best, the psychotic symptoms of schizophrenia may result from a functional increase (for example, an increased "turnover" or receptor number) in dopamine function. The exact etiologic factors responsible for an increase in DA function in schizophrenia are still unknown. The important point is that a series of rather sophisticated clinical studies (PET, plasma HVA, and so forth) have evolved from very careful pharmacologic and neurochemical experiments and seem to confirm the animal data.

CONCLUSIONS

I have attempted to give a few examples of how basic neuroscience research has been integrated into clinical psychiatry. The past decade has witnessed the generation of an impressive amount of new data on the basic mechanisms of nervous system activity. Much has already been learned by applying this information to the study of abnormal human behavior, but, undoubtedly, we are just beginning!

References

1. Coyle JT, Price DL, DeLong MR: Alzheimer's disease: a disorder of cholinergic innervation of cortex. Science 219:1184–1190, 1983

2. Pickar D, Labarca R, Linnoila M, et al.: Neuroleptic-induced decrease in plasma homovanillic acid and antipsychotic activity in schizophrenic patients. Science 225:954–957, 1984

3. Paul SM, Janowsky A, Skolnick P: Monoaminergic neurotransmitters and antidepressant drugs, in Psychiatry Update: The American Psychiatric Association Annual Review, vol 4. Edited by Hales RE, Frances AJ. Washington, DC, American Psychiatric Press, 1985

4. Ninan PT, Insel TM, Cohen RM, et al.: Benzodiazepine receptor-mediated experimental "anxiety" in primates. Science 218:1332–1334, 1982

5. Watson SJ, Kelsey JE, Lopez JF, et al.: Neuropeptide biology: basic and clinical lessons from the opioids, in Psychiatry Update: The American Psychiatric Association Annual Review, vol 4. Edited by Hales RE, Frances AJ. Washington, DC, American Psychiatric Press, 1985

6. Hays SE, Paul SM: CCK receptors and human neurological disease. Life Sci 31:319–322, 1982

7. Hökfelt T, Rehfeld JF, Skirboll LR, et al.: Evidence for coexistence of dopamine and CCK in meso-limbic neurons. Nature 285:476–478, 1980

8. Skirboll LR, Grace AA, Hommer DW, et al.: Peptide-monoamine coexistence: studies of the actions of cholecystokinin-like peptide on the electrical activity of midbrain dopamine neurons. Neuroscience 6:2111–2124, 1981

9. Crawley JN, Stivers JA, Blumstein LK, et al.: Cholecystokinin potentiates dopamine-mediated behaviors: evidence for modulation specific to a site of co-existence. J Neurosci (in press)

10. Creese I, Burt DR, Snyder SH: Dopamine receptor binding predicts clinical and pharmacological potencies of antischizophrenic drugs. Science 192:481–483, 1976

11. Seeman P, Lee T, Chau-Wong M, et al.: Antipsychotic drug doses and neuroleptic/dopamine receptors. Nature 261:717–719, 1976

12. Snyder SH, Banerjee SP, Yamamura HI, et al.: Drugs, neurotransmitters and schizophrenia. Science 184:1243–1253, 1974

13. Lee T, Seeman P, Tourtellotte W, et al.: Binding of ^{3}H–neuroleptics and ^{3}H–apomorphine in schizophrenic brains. Nature 274:897–900, 1978

14. Mackay AVP, Bird ED, Spokes EG, et al.: Dopamine receptors and schizophrenia: drug effect or illness? Lancet 2:915–916, 1980

15. Seeman P: Brain dopamine receptors. Pharmacol Rev 32:229–313, 1980

16. Wagner HH Jr, Burns HD, Dannals RF, et al.: Imaging dopamine receptors in the brain by positron tomography. Science 221:1264–1266, 1983

17. Chiodo LA, Bunney BS: Typical and atypical neuroleptics: differential effects of chronic administration on the activity of A9 and A10 midbrain dopaminergic neurons. J Neurosci 3:1607–1619, 1983

18. White FJ, Wang RY: Differential effects of classical and atypical antipsychotic drugs on A9 and A10 dopamine neurons. Science 221: 1054–1056, 1983

4

Huntington's Disease and the New Genetics: A Preview of the Future for Psychiatric Disorders

Nancy S. Wexler, Ph.D.
James F. Gusella, Ph.D.
P. Michael Conneally, Ph.D.
David Housman, Ph.D.

4

Huntington's Disease and the New Genetics: A Preview of the Future for Psychiatric Disorders

Modern science is traversing traditional disciplinary boundaries, creating an interdisciplinary cadre of researchers, and developing new, unified strategies for investigating seemingly diverse disorders. Molecular genetic techniques, developed only in the last decade, are applicable to any disease with a hereditary component, be it familial hypercholestrolemia, cystic fibrosis, manic depressive disorder, or Huntington's disease. Recent advances in Huntington's disease research have confirmed the power of these new techniques to locate genes and, hopefully, eventually to isolate and characterize mutant genes. Molecular genetic methodologies should soon be able to clarify the genetics of the major psychiatric disorders.

An elucidation of Huntington's disease should be particularly illuminating to other neuropsychiatric disorders. The dramatic movement disorders of this illness are clearly neurological, but the equally prominent, and perhaps more devastating, disturbances of cognition and mood are the domain of the psychiatrist. Like Alzheimer's disease, Parkinson's disease, Gilles de la Tourette syndrome, and other disorders with neurologic and psychiatric features, Huntington's disease demands interdisciplinary research and clinical expertise; unlike the other diseases, it too often falls through the proverbial disciplinary cracks. The story behind Huntington's disease should tell us a great deal about mind/body relationships. We anticipate that it will soon be possible to understand the etiology and pathology of the illness, from the message in the mutated gene itself to its impact on target tissues in the brain. This path from gene to brain will surely bridge many disciplines and, hopefully, will be useful to investigators of other diseases.

CLINICAL CHARACTERISTICS OF HUNTINGTON'S DISEASE

Huntington's disease is a progressive and fatal neuropsychiatric disorder characterized by involuntary movements, intellectual decline, and severe personality and mood disturbances. It is inherited as an autosomal dominant disease and usually appears in the third or fourth decade of life but may appear as early as the first or as late as the eighth. The gene is fully penetrant and will always be expressed if the carrier lives long enough. There are no documented cases of a new mutation, although some putative ones have been reported. Because the illness usually does not appear until after children are produced, voluntary abstinence from childbearing is the only way to eliminate the deleterious gene from the gene pool. It is possible that only one or a few mutations occurring in antiquity have been passed down through the ages and have spread across the world through trade and migration. Huntington's disease is found predominantly in Caucasians with a prevalence rate of approximately one in ten thousand. Somewhat smaller prevalence rates have been reported in black and Oriental populations (1).

The disease originally was called Huntington's chorea after George Huntington, the Long Island doctor who, in 1862, first described the illness and its hereditary pattern (2). Chorea, which like the word choreography stems from the Greek word for dance, depicts the primary movement pathology found in the illness.

Other types of movement disorders appear during the 10- to 20-year duration of the disease. Oculomotor disturbances and choreic adventitious movements are the earliest manifestations; dystonia and parkinsonian symptoms appear several years later. Dysarthria leads eventually to incoherent speech or mutism, while dysphagia results in severe, often fatal, choking. A pronounced urgency to eat is accompanied by weight loss and cachexia. After years of exhausting illness, patients eventually succumb to aspiration pneumonia or heart disease (3). George Huntington was astute in pointing out, in the only published paper of his career, that the psychiatric symptoms of Huntington's disease are even more devastating than the physical ones, bizarre and arresting as the writhing and gesticulations may be. Huntington described the illness as "that insanity tending towards suicide" (2). The name was changed to Huntington's disease to better encompass the psychological aspects of the disorder.

Cognitive impairment is often an early sign of the illness. Short-term memory deteriorates first; after some time, long-term memory is also affected. The capacity to organize and sequence events is disrupted and arithmetic ability is impaired. Attention is easily distracted. Although old tasks can be maintained for quite some time, new learning is difficult. Language function is well preserved despite marked decreases in word fluency. Unlike patients with Alzheimer's disease, patients with Huntington's disease maintain insight and orientation, often until death. They remember people who are emotionally meaningful to them and may preserve a sense of humor until very advanced stages of the illness (4). Since Huntington's disease affects primarily the basal ganglia with very little cortical involvement, it has been described as a "subcortical dementia" (3).

Personality disturbances may precede the appearance of involuntary movements in more than one-half of the patients and by as much as 20 years. Apathy, irritability and withdrawal, explosive temper outbursts, and emotional lability are frequent early signs. Depression, often severe and suicidal, is a common symptom both prodromally and after the movements emerge. The majority of patients have unipolar depression, according to *DSM-III* criteria, although some have bipolar (manic-depressive) disease. A small number manifest symptoms of schizophrenia, including hallucinations, delusions, and paranoid ideation (5). The cognitive and emotional disturbances caused by Huntington's disease are often what is most distressing to patients and families. Although abnormal movements are incapacitating and socially embarrassing, the psychiatric manifestations are often the most debilitating.

Conduct disorder once was thought to be premonitory for the later development of Huntington's disease. Folstein et al. (6) studied the cohesiveness and stability of families affected by Huntington's disease. In disorganized, volatile, and fragmented families, many of the children demonstrated conduct disorder. Some subsequently developed the illness, while others did not. However, in well organized, intact families, conduct disorders did not occur in either the presymptomatic or normal offspring.

The primary target of the genetically programmed cell death of Huntington's disease is in the basal ganglia, particularly the caudate nucleus and putamen. Thalamus, hypothalamus, and areas of the brain stem are also affected. A variety of neurotransmitters and their associated enzymes and neuropeptides are depleted in these damaged brain areas—primarily gamma-aminobutyric acid, acetylcholine, substance-P, and cholecystokinin. Somatostatin is increased in the basal ganglia; dopamine and glutamate levels are relatively unchanged (7).

Reactions to the psychiatric symptomatology that is an endogenous component of the illness can be profound. Until recently, there was no way to determine if a person at-risk was carrying the lethal gene until symptoms of the disease appeared, usually in midlife. Because the initial symptoms are extremely subtle and insidious and the range of onset is very broad, life can be marred by a state of chronic anxiety and stress. Once diagnosed, the patient may experience intense guilt over the possibility of transmitting the disorder to children and grandchildren. The high suicide rate among Huntington's disease patients, five to seven times above the national average (5), may be a reflection of these stresses coupled with the patient's keen perception of deteriorating capacities in a mind with insight well preserved.

RECOMBINANT DNA TECHNIQUES AND GENE LINKAGE

Research interest in Huntington's disease increased steadily during the 1970s. A variety of neurochemical hypotheses were pursued and an intense search of peripheral tissue for the putative etiological culprit was undertaken. Yet by the end of the decade, many promising leads had proved to be negative or, at best, equivocal. During the same period, however, spectacular advances in molecular genetics were being developed that would make it feasible to use the genetic nature of Huntington's disease, its one immutable characteristic, as the entry to its elucidation. These advances included the marriage that occurred in the late 1970s between the most sophisticated recombinant DNA techniques and traditional methods of gene linkage.

Gene linkage is based on the principle that two genes lying close to each other on a chromosome will tend to be inherited together. If one cannot find a gene of interest using other techniques, one can attempt to locate another gene with more identifiable characteristics that is quite close to it on the same chromosome. If the two genes are physically close together, they will most likely remain together during meiotic division; such genes are said to be "linked." The identifiable gene is termed the "marker" because it marks the locale where the gene of interest—a disease-causing gene, for example—can be found. If the linkage between the two genes is tight, the marker gene can be almost as good an indicator of the presence of the gene causing disease as that gene itself (8).

In gametic formation, a pair of chromosomes will recombine to exchange genetic material. If linkage is loose—that is, if some distance separates the marker and the disease gene—there is a chance that when the two homologous chromosomes recombine during meiosis, the marker and the disease gene will separate. The greater the distance, the more likely it is that a break or recombination will occur between the marker and the disease gene. One can calculate statistically the probability of recombination, which can be considered the potential "error rate" in using the marker to predict the presence of the disease gene. If the distance is too great between the marker and the disease gene, the likelihood of recombination will be too high, and the marker will not be useful. Genes far away from each other on the same chromosome or on different chromosomes well segregate independently.

By 1979, the 30 or more classical polymorphic antigen and enzyme markers already in existence had been analyzed for genetic linkage to the Huntington's disease gene with uniformly negative results. Although these studies eliminated approximately 20 percent of the genome from analysis, the supply of existing markers for which to search was depleted and progress in generating new ones was very slow (1). The research terrain was looking bleak.

The advent of recombinant DNA changed all this. A close examination of DNA itself revealed the presence of structural variations that are polymorphic in the sequence of base pairs throughout the genome. There are vast numbers of these base pair differences and, for the most part, they appear benign. Some of these base pair changes occur in the cutting sites for restriction enzymes (8–11). Much of recombinant DNA technology was made possible by the discovery that certain bacteria have enzymes, called restriction enzymes, which will cut DNA when they recognize a particular sequence of base pairs—for example, four, six, eight, or 10 bases in a particular order—that signals them to cut. If a change of base pairs occurs in a recognition site, altering the order of base pairs, the enzyme will not recognize the new sequence and will not cut at this site (8–11).

When DNA is exposed to these enzymes in a laboratory experiment, it will be cut into a multitude of fragments of varying lengths. If two persons vary in their recognition sites, their DNA is cut into fragments of different lengths. These DNA fragments are then separated by size using agarose gel electrophoresis. The small, light fragments migrate quickly to the bottom of the gel, while larger, heavier fragments remain toward the top (8–11). DNA on a gel looks like a continuum made up of millions of fragments of DNA. In order to visualize particular fragments of DNA, a probe must be used. A probe is a specific, unique piece of DNA whose chromosomal location may or may not be known. It is analogous to a specific stain used in ordinary electrophoresis and is used to

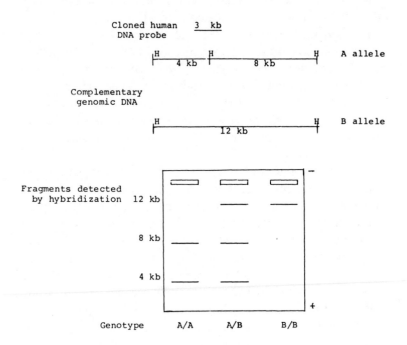

Figure 1. An example of a restriction fragment length polymorphism (RFLP).
A cloned 3 kb copy sequence of human DNA (called a probe) can
detect the presence or absence of a polymorphic Hind III (H) site. If
the variable site is present, DNA is cleaved at the site and two
fragments of 4 and 8 kb are produced. This is the A allele at this
locus. The B allele is a 12 kb fragment which results when the
variable Hind III site is missing. A person's marker type at a particular locus is revealed through Southern blotting techniques. Human
genomic DNA is digested to completion with bacterial enzyme
Hind III. Fragments are separated by agarose gel electrophoresis,
denatured, then hybridized with a radioactive probe. Autoradiography detects where the probe reanneals with complementary genomic DNA on the gel. The gel in the figure demonstrates three
possible genotypes at the marker locus; haplotypes for both chromosomes of a pair are shown.

detect fragments from a particular area of a chromosome. The probe is made radioactive so that it can be visualized easily and is denatured—that is, separated into single strands. The gel containing DNA is also denatured, leaving only a single strand of DNA clinging to the gel paper. When the radioactive probe is applied to the gel, the probe's DNA will seek its complementary strand on the gel and reanneal, emitting its radioactive signal so that its presence can be detected (8–11).

In the region of chromosomal DNA corresponding to the probe, one person may have one recognition site for a particular enzyme, creating two fragments when cut, while another person may have none, creating one fragment when cut. The differences between the two persons will be visualized when the probe anneals to their respective DNA. In the first individual, two bands of different size will appear, while in the second individual, only one band will appear. These differences are stable and heritable, just as any other genetic trait is. Because these fragment-length-pattern differences can be visualized, they can serve as markers in the human genome. They are called restriction fragment-length polymorphisms (RFLPs) and provide a rich supply of new markers to test for linkage. Markers are then localized to specific regions on particular chromosomes using *in situ* hybridization techniques. If a marker is localized to chromosome four, for example, a gene linked to that marker must also be on chromosome four. In this way, unique sequence RFLP markers can serve to develop a "surveyor's grid" to map the human genome (8–10).

In order for RFLP markers to be useful in detecting the presence of a disease gene, the marker and the disease phenotype (which is the expression of the disease genotype) must be shown to segregate together in a pedigree (9–11). For example, if a DNA marker is linked closely to the Huntington's disease gene, and the affected parent is heterozygous for the marker (in other words, has two forms of the marker), then all persons with the gene in that family should have one particular form of the marker, while their unaffected brothers and sisters should have the other. It is necessary for linkage analysis to look first within a family, because it is certain that the disease gene is the same and in the same position on a chromosome in all members of one family. It is important to study a large family in which the persons affected by the disease have many relatives who have lived symptom-free beyond the age of high risk. Thus, in a family with Huntington's disease, one would study all those with the disease, since they clearly have the gene, and their unaffected siblings, age 55 years and older, who have less than a five or 10 percent chance of having the gene. Obviously, the size and structure of the families to be studied are critical to the success of the endeavor (11).

APPLICATION OF MOLECULAR GENETICS TO HUNTINGTON'S DISEASE

In 1979, the Hereditary Disease Foundation sponsored a workshop at the National Institutes of Health in which scientists who were involved in recombinant DNA technology, somatic cell genetics, and population genetics and clinicians who were knowledgeable about Huntington's disease, were brought together to explore the use of the new recombinant DNA technologies in locating the Huntington's disease gene. Since the nearness of a particular marker to the Huntington's disease gene is an event of chance, workshop participants thought it might be necessary to generate as many as 600 to 800 different RFLP DNA markers to locate one near the Huntington's disease gene. David Housman, one of the present authors, was a cochair of the workshop as well as a developer and ardent proponent of these new techniques. Although only two RFLP markers were in existence at the time, a steadfast conviction in the theoretical accuracy of the plan gave workshop participants an exuberant confidence in the power of this new technology for solving genetic questions.

With seed money from the Hereditary Disease Foundation and a subsequent grant from the National Institute of Neurological and Communicative Disorders and Stroke to James Gusella, the quest to find the Huntington's disease gene began. The initial task was locating the most appropriate families to study. The largest United States family with Huntington's disease was located by the National Research Roster for Huntington's Disease Patients and

Families, administered by P. Michael Conneally at the University of Indiana. Blood samples for DNA extraction were collected from appropriate family members.

Another family of promising size had been brought to our attention in 1972 by Dr. Ramon Avilá-Girón (12). This family lived in three isolated villages along the shores of Lake Maracaibo in Venezuela. In 1955, Dr. Américo Negrette, a Venezuelan bio-chemist and internist, had accurately diagnosed and described Huntington's disease in this large, extended family. Perceiving correctly that there was a single common ancestor who had trans-mitted the gene, Negrette constructed a pedigree of the family that contained several hundred persons. In the late 1970s, Nancy Wexler, while serving as Executive Director of the Congressional Commission for the Control of Huntington's Disease and Its Con-sequences, began negotiations with the Venezuelan University of Zulia to continue the study. When we began our work in 1979, in collaboration with Drs. Américo Negrette, Ramon Avilá-Girón, Ernesto Bonilla, and Humberto Moreno, among others, none of us were aware that the family was as large as it ultimately proved to be. We did know, however, that it was large enough to be of interest in collecting data for genetic linkage analysis.

From 1980 to the present, each March a small group of investi-gators including Drs. Anne B. Young, John B. Penney, and Simon Starosta (University of Michigan), Ira Shoulson (University of Rochester), Fidela Gomez, R.N. (Miami), Helen Travers, M.S. (University of Miami), and Nancy Wexler, one of the authors, traveled to Venezuela to study this family. The family has been a superb research resource. The pedigree, taken entirely through oral report, dates from the early 1800s; it now numbers 3,529 persons, more than 3,000 of whom are still alive. The Hunting-ton's disease gene has been traced to a single individual living in the early 1800s in a stilt village along the lake. The origin of the gene in the founder of this pedigree is unknown. The family includes 88 persons with Huntington's disease and 1,536 persons who, because they have either a parent or grandparent with the disease, have either a 50 percent or 25 percent risk of developing the disorder. Since the majority of the at-risk population is under the age of 40 in the period of highest risk, the potential health threat to the area is quite alarming. Many unique features of this extended family make it an ideal resource to study. Because none of the patients take any medication usually prescribed for Huntington's disease, the natural history of the illness can be described in its purest form. All patients share exactly the same environment, including climate (high heat and humidity), diet, environmental pathogens, and culture. These environmental controls make the genetic influences more obvious.

In this family we observed every phenotypic variation of Huntington's disease, including juvenile to late onset, rigid and choreic forms, severe to moderate psychiatric or intellectual involvement, rapid to prolonged decline. This diversity exists even though all members of the family have inherited the same gene and share the same environment. If our research team had not known that all these varying phenotypes were manifestations of the same HD genotype, we might have been tempted to subdivide each category into its purest form. In psychiatric disorders, the phenotype is often all that is available to an investigator. There are many instances in which members of the same family are affected by different psychiatric illnesses. Clinically, these diseases seem to be separate entities even though they appear in the same family. Perhaps when the genetics of these disorders are better understood, it will be discovered that many different phenotypes are variable expressions of the same underlying genotype.

The presence of numerous subpopulations within the family in Venezuela further enhance potential research benefits. There are multiple instances of two and three generations in the same family who are simultaneously symptomatic. There also are twin pairs, both dizygous and concordant and monozygous and concordant for the illness. Other twin pairs are still too young to express the disease. Approximately 10 percent of the population has the juvenile form of the illness, including one girl who has already borne three children. Sibship size is commonly 10 or more children. One of the largest families has 14 children and 62 grandchildren and great-grandchildren. There are also a fair number of consanguienous unions, with both parents affected or at risk, providing the possibility of locating someone homozygous for HD.

Each patient and person at risk whose blood was sampled for genetic analysis was given a neurological examination and assigned to a stage of functional capacity according to a scale developed by Shoulson and Fahn (13). Folstein Mini Mental examination for dementia was adapted for a Spanish-speaking, nonliterate population; it was administered in concert with the Purdue Pegboard exam for testing manual dexterity and a picture test of our own design for memory, recall, and recognition. The cognitive tests have value mostly as measure of longitudinal change. The difficulties in overcoming obstacles created by cross cultural differences are impressive.

Almost 800 blood samples (from which transformed lymphocyte lines were made) and slightly fewer fibrolasts have been collected from nuclear families within this extended pedigree. The majority of the cells are available through the NIGMS Human Genetic Mutant Cell Repository in Camden, New Jersey (14). The nuclear family sizes are so large that they are valuable as "reference pedigrees," which can be used to study segregation patterns of genetic material in general, in addition to that of the Huntington's disease gene.

It was the power of both the numbers and structure of this Venezuelan family that confirmed linkage of the RFLP marker known as G8 (characterized by James Gusella) to the Huntington's disease gene (15). The marker G8, and thus the HD gene, was localized to chromosome four (15). In families in which the Huntington's disease gene is linked to the marker G8, the probability of inheritance can be changed from 50:50 for a person at risk to 95:5. This means that there are approximately five million base pairs between the marker G8 and the HD gene on chromosome four.

G8 is a four allele marker produced when DNA is exposed to the restriction enzyme Hind III. There are two sites in the marker G8 that the enzyme Hind III variably cuts or does not cut.

The presence or absence of cuts at these sites in combination produces four different pattern types which a person can have at the G8 locus. These types are known as haplotypes A, B, C, and D.

G8 MARKER

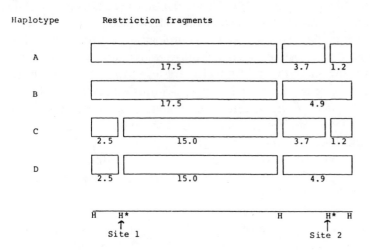

Figure 2. Haplotypes at the G8 locus. The (H) indicates an invariable cleavage site with Hind III, while H* indicates a variable site. The presence or absence of the two H* sites produces two possible alleles. Combining these two closely linked alleles forms a haplotype. There are four possible alleles at the G8 locus: A (−,+), B (−,−), C (+,+), D (+,−).

In the Venezuelan kindred, the chromosome bearing the HD gene carries the haplotype C of the marker G8, while in the largest U.S family, the chromosome carrying the haplotype A is indicative of the presence of the HD gene.

USING THE MARKER FOR DIAGNOSIS: QUESTIONS

A major question that must be resolved before this marker can be used to diagnose Huntington's disease presymptomatically or pre-natally is that of genetic heterogeneity. Is there only one Hunting-ton's disease gene, which will always be found in the same place on chromosome four linked to G8, or are there many different genes, some of which may be located on different chromosomes entirely? Just as one genotype can produce great variations in phenotype, often similar phenotypes can be the result of varying genotypes. At present, we are studying a number of families with Huntington's disease throughout the world with as many different racial and ethnic backgrounds as possible. If 20 or more of these families prove to have the G8 marker linked to the Huntington's disease gene, then it will be ethically acceptable to use this marker as a test for the gene, even though a given family may not be large enough to prove linkage definitively.

A number of factors influence the informativeness of the marker test for presymptomatic and prenatal diagnosis. First, if the

KEY:

squares: males
circles: females
black circle or squares:
    inherited HD
diagonal line: deceased

The marker pattern on chromosome 4: AA, AB, BB is shown under each person. One pattern comes from the mother, the other from the father.

Figure 3A. Pedigree 1—Informative. This pedigree can be used for presymptomatic diagnosis. On one chromosome 4, the father with HD has marker pattern B and a normal gene which he inherited from his normal father. His father could only give pattern B. His other chromosome 4 has marker pattern A. Marker pattern A must have come from his mother. Marker pattern A and the HD gene are "traveling" together. The daughter received marker pattern A from both her normal mother and her HD father. Pattern A from the father signifies that the HD gene is present. She thus has a 95% chance of having received the HD gene also. The reason it is not 100% is that there is about a 5% chance that a "crossover" or exchange took place which would cause the HD gene to travel with the marker pattern B. This pedigree assumes that the HD gene is on chromosome 4. Reprinted from Wexler NS, Conneally PM, Guselle JF: Huntington's Discovery "Fact Sheet." Santa Monica, CA, Hereditary Disease Foundation, 1984. Reprinted courtesy of the Hereditary Disease Foundation. All rights reserved.

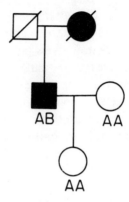

Figure 3B. Pedigree 2—Uninformative. This pedigree cannot be used for presymptomatic diagnosis. We cannot tell whether the HD gene goes with marker pattern A or B since there is no information on the grandparents. The marker is not helpful. Reprinted from Wexler NS, Conneally PM, Guselle JF: Huntington's Discovery "Fact Sheet." Santa Monica, CA, Hereditary Disease Foundation, 1984. Reprinted courtesy of the Hereditary Disease Foundation. All rights reserved.

affected parent is homozygous for the marker, it is impossible to tell whether an offspring inherited the chromosome four containing the normal gene or the mutant allele. Improvements in making the haplotypes more complex by combining them with other haplotypes, a combination produced by different enzymes cutting within the same general area, should make it increasingly easier to differentiate one homologous chromosome from the other since people are unlikely to share identical, very complicated haplotypes. Second, the possibility of recombination introduces uncertainties into the test. Discovery of a flanking marker on the other side of the Huntington's disease gene should reduce error caused by recombination, as it is exceedingly unlikely that there will be a double recombination, between both flanking markers and the gene itself. A third difficulty in using this marker test diagnostically concerns the availability of genetically informative relatives to determine which haplotype of the marker is "traveling" with the Huntington's disease gene. Because Huntington's disease is fatal, often the affected parent has died by the time his or her children are interested in presymptomatic or prenatal detection. Until a test is available, it is possible to store DNA samples from affected and unaffected relatives, who are needed to provide genetic information. DNA also can be obtained from a variety of tissues, including frozen brain and skin biopsy. The first human DNA bank in the United States has been established at Indiana University to begin to provide this necessary service.

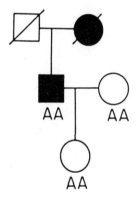

Figure 3C. Pedigree 3—Uninformative. This pedigree also cannot be used for presymptomatic diagnosis. The affected parent has marker pattern A on both chromosome 4s. Since her mother and father both gave her pattern A and there is currently no way to tell which A came from whom, it is impossible to tell which A was passed to the at-risk daughter—the A near the normal gene or near the HD gene. This pedigree could not be used for counseling the daughter even if the grandparent's marker types were known. Reprinted from Wexler NS, Conneally PM, Guselle JF: Huntington's Discovery "Fact Sheet." Santa Monica, CA, Hereditary Disease Foundation, 1984. Reprinted courtesy of the Hereditary Disease Foundation. All rights reserved.

Even with the DNA bank facilities, some families will be too small to permit presymptomatic identification of the Huntington's disease gene carrier. Members of these families may wish to know if they can have children who they can be confident will be free of the illness. Some who would like to know if their children will be free of the disorder will not wish to know if they, themselves, will be affected. Possibilities exist for providing useful information. If the Huntington's disease gene is on chromosome four, it need only be determined whether a fetus inherits a chromosome four from its affected grandparent or from the unaffected spouse of the affected grandparent. The fetus's other chromosome four will come from the other grandparent couple. If the fetus inherits the chromosome four from the unaffected grandparent, its risk—limited to that of possible recombination—will be very

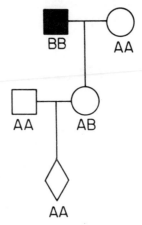

Figure 3D. Pedigree 4—Prenatal counseling. The diamond represents a fetus. In this case, we can tell that the fetus inherited marker pattern A from its mother who in turn inherited this same marker from her mother together with a normal gene. The chance that the fetus carries the HD gene is low (less than three percent). On the other hand, if the fetus is AB it has a 50–50 chance of carrying the HD gene. In either case, the mother's risk is still 50–50. Reprinted from Wexler NS, Conneally PM, Guselle JF: Huntington's Discovery "Fact Sheet." Santa Monica, CA, Hereditary Disease Foundation, 1984. Reprinted courtesy of the Hereditary Disease Foundation. All rights reserved.

small. If the fetus inherits a chromosome four from the grandparent with Huntington's disease, its risk is 50:50 since it is not known whether the chromosome four passed down to the fetus is the one carrying the Huntington's disease allele or the one with its normal counterpart. The fetus has the same risk as its at-risk parent, who also has one chromosome four from his or her affected parent. Fetal DNA determination can be made through amniocentesis, and the prospective parents can be advised whether the fetus has an essentially zero risk or a 50:50 risk of developing Huntington's disease. This can be done without altering knowledge of the odds for the at-risk parent in any way. Also, it only requires DNA samples from the two prospective parents, one or both parents of the at-risk partner, and the fetus (16-18).

USING THE MARKER: PRACTICAL AND ETHICAL IMPLICATIONS

The prospect of prenatal and presymptomatic diagnostic counseling for Huntington's disease is opening up a new era in medical progress. The capacity to diagnose, far in advance of the appearance of an illness, the certain development of a fatal, progressive, neurodegenerative disorder for which there is no treatment is unprecedented. Clearly, it is much simpler to discuss the nuances of meiosis and haplotypes, and the vagaries of recombination fractions than to face the overwhelming impact this information will have on human lives (19).

The linkage test for the presence or absence of the HD gene makes the process all the more complex because family members' cooperation must be solicited and obtained in order for the test to be run. A family diagnosis as well as an individual one must be made. For example, a 45-year-old, at-risk woman may be at peace with her at-risk status and may prefer not to know her carrier status. Her son, age 22, is married and wishes to begin a family. The son cannot be tested without a sample of the mother's DNA. If the son is found to be free of the illness, it says nothing about the mother's carrier status since she could have the gene but not have passed it on to him. If the son is found to have the marker type indicating the presence of the Huntington's disease gene, the mother is an obligate carrier. The mother's diagnosis is then contained within the son's.

There may be intense pressure to push at-risk individuals either toward or away from testing. If a father who is at risk chooses not to be tested, his wife may pressure him to find out for the sake of knowing about their children's future. If the father is free, the children also are free of the gene. A husband of a woman at risk may pressure his wife to be tested in order to make better financial plans for her and the children. All members of the family have their own particular agendas, needs, and demands.

One determining factor in people's reactions to presymptomatic diagnostic testing is their personal experience with the illness. In some families, an affected relative may leave home early and die in an obscure hospital far away. Family members may never have seen someone with advanced Huntington's disease. These people may plunge ahead with diagnostic testing, only to get a good look at the disorder after learning the stark truth about themselves. Other families have seen numerous members progress and die from the disease. Because of the late onset of the illness, young adults, who seem to be the people most eager to be tested, often have parents in the final stages of Huntington's disease. These at-risk persons are faced with the prospect of coming home to a dying parent after learning that this fate has been programmed in their own genes. In speaking of their intentions to be tested, some persons at risk seem to be acting on bravado and "macho" recklessness, while others are filled with terror and anxiety at the mere prospect of testing. Many have a realistic appraisal of the test's benefits and dangers, and all express some amount of apprehension. It will be crucial to work intensively and sensitively with people at risk to help them make the most appropriate decisions about whether or not to be tested and how to cope with the information learned.

Questions of continuation of insurance coverage, use of insurance to pay for testing, confidentiality of test results, and employer leverage to insist on testing are all areas of uncertainty. The manner in which these questions are resolved will have an impact not only on testing for Huntington's disease but also on future testing for all hereditary disorders.

Maximal support will be necessary for those who are found to have the gene. All persons coming for testing preferably should be accompanied by someone who can be available either during or after the test. If necessary, the counselor providing diagnostic information should be in touch with the individual later on the same day as the results are given. In the following days and months, personal and telephone contacts should be made daily, weekly, or monthly, as is required. An entire range of services must be available to persons receiving test information, including the following: crisis phones for emergency calls; individual counseling; group therapy (preferably with others who have received the same test results but including some sessions with those who received opposite results); physical rehabilitation and nutritional planning to better prepare for the future; and other educational groups to make sure that people understand the information they were given and its potential legal and financial implications. People should be free to choose among the services but should be encouraged to participate in as many as possible, if only to occupy their minds during a period of shock and stress and keep them in contact with the therapeutic community. The legal rights, particularly the confidentiality, of those found to be presymptomatic must be protected.

At-risk persons who escape inheriting the Huntington's disease gene must not be ignored. While their exuberance is to be expected, so is some depression and guilt. They may have brothers and sisters, cousins, and other relatives who are not so lucky. As seen in research on the psychological casualties of war, the guilt of the survivor is a strong psychological dynamic. Also, identities, which have been built on the knowledge of being at risk, must now be reshaped. Being at risk may have had certain secondary gains that have become woven into the fabric of a person's life. Special dispensations and concessions will no longer be tolerated, and the at-risk person may paradoxically find him- or herself in a situation of new and perhaps unwanted responsibility and freedom. No longer will he or she be able to blame irritability, depression, clumsiness, or any other characteristic on possible early signs of Huntington's disease. Options such as love, children, and career will become available to one who was previously reluctant to engage in the face of an uncertain future. This freedom may impose stress as well as joy.

Few people in the mental health professions are equipped to handle complex counseling of this nature. Those trained in genetics are, by and large, unsophisticated about psychotherapeutic theory or technique. Psychotherapists, on the other hand, are equally naive about genetics. Few persons are skilled in both areas and can provide the necessary counseling, which, as a requirement, must accompany presymptomatic testing. How these services will be financed is another question which must be resolved on behalf of Huntington's disease and other hereditary disorders.

CONCLUSIONS

A startling prospect is opening before us: the prediction of life and death through careful scrutiny of the genes before any other telltale evidence appears. For the first time, there is a realistic expectation that the burden of morbidity and mortality from this dreadful disorder can be reduced. Yet we are confronted with unique challenges inherent in the prospect of a presymptomatic diagnosis for a fatal, progressive, midlife degenerative disorder for which there is no treatment. How creatively we handle these questions and how intelligently and thoroughly we safeguard those who come for help will have a profound influence on the future.

References

1. Conneally PM: Huntington's disease: genetics and epidemiology. Am J Hum Genet 36:506–526, 1984

2. Huntington G: On chorea. Medical and Surgical Reporter 26: 317–321, 1872

3. Shoulson I: Care of patients and families with Huntington's disease,

in Neurology, vol. 2: Movement Disorders. Edited by Marsden CD, Fahn S. Stoneham, MA, Butterworth Scientific (International Medical Review Series), 1982

4. Wexler NS: Perceptual motor, cognitive, and emotional characteristics of persons at risk for Huntington's disease, in Huntington's Disease: Advances in Neurology, vol. 23. Edited by Chase TN, Wexler NS, Barbeau A. New York, Raven Press, 1979

5. Folstein SE, Folstein MF: Psychiatric features of Huntington's disease. Psychiatric Developments 1(2):193–206, 1983

6. Folstein SE, Franz ML, Jensen BA, et al.: Conduct disorder and affective disorder among the offspring of patients with Huntington's disease. Psychol Med 13:45–52, 1983

7. Shoulson I: Huntington's disease: a decade of progress. Neurologic Clinics 2(3):515–526, 1984

8. Botstein D, White RL, Skolnick M, et al.: Construction of a genetic linkage map in man using restriction fragment length polymorphisms. Am J Hum Genet 32:314–331, 1980

9. Housman D, Gusella JF: Application of recombinant DNA techniques to neurogenetic disorders, in Genetics of Neurological and Psychiatric Diseases. Edited by Kety S, Rowland LP, Sidman RL, et al. New York, Raven Press, 1983

10. Gusella JF, Tanzi R, Anderson MA, et al.: Recombinant DNA application to human disease, in Banbury Report Series, vol. 14. Edited by Caskey CT, White RL. New York, Cold Spring Harbor Laboratory, 1983

11. Gusella JF, Tanzi RE, Anderson MA, et al.: DNA markers for nervous system diseases. Sciences 225:1320-1326, 1984

12. Avilá Girón R: Medical and social aspects of Huntington's chorea in the state of Zulia, Venezuela, in Advances in Neurology, vol. 1: Huntington's Chorea 1872–1972. Edited by Barbeau A, Chase TN, Paulson GW. New York, Raven Press, 1973

13. Shoulson I, Fahn S: Huntington's disease: clinical care and evaluation. Neurology 29:1–3, 1979

14. NIGMS Human Genetics Mutant Cell Repository: 1984 Catalogue of Cell Lines. Camden, New Jersey, Institute for Medical Research (609-966-7377)

15. Gusella JF, Wexler NS, Conneally PM, et al.: A polymorphic DNA marker genetically linked to Huntington's disease. Nature 306:234–238, 1983

16. Conneally PM, Wallace MR, Gusella JF, et al.: Huntington's disease: estimation of heterozygote status using linked genetic markers. Genetic Epidemiology 1:81–88, 1984

17. Wexler NS, Conneally PM, Gusella JF: Huntington's Discovery "Fact Sheet." Santa Monica, CA, Hereditary Disease Foundation, 1984

18. Wexler NS, Conneally PM, Housman D, et al.: A DNA polymorphism for Huntington's disease marks the future. Arch Neurol 42:20–24, 1985

19. Wexler NS: Genetic jeopardy and the new clairvoyance, in Medical Genetics: Genetics of Neurological Disorders. Edited by Bearn A, Motulsky A, Childs B. Philadelphia, Praeger Press, 1985 (in press)

5

Research at the Interface of Psychiatry and Medicine

Harold Alan Pincus, M.D.
David R. Rubinow, M.D.

5

Research at the Interface of Psychiatry and Medicine

Over the past several decades the convergence of psychiatry and the rest of medicine has become increasingly evident. The rapprochement has been fostered by a series of scientific and political developments ranging from advances in biological psychiatry and behavioral medicine to the recommendations of Presidential (1) and National Academy (2) Commissions. The development of new tools and techniques in the neurosciences and the growth of psychiatric consultation-liaison programs represent major interfaces between general medicine and psychiatry at both the basic science and clinical services levels.

Despite these linkages the relationship between consultation-liaison psychiatry and biological psychiatric research has remained underdeveloped. This is particularly surprising because there currently exist numerous opportunities to utilize the new techniques and tools of the neurosciences to study the relationship between psychiatric and medical conditions—the central thrust of consultation-liaison psychiatry.

This chapter will examine recent professional and political forces that have drawn attention to the interface of behavioral and general medical concerns; describe several models that illustrate the relationship between medical and psychiatric conditions;

present specific research questions that require techniques and strategies of the neurosciences and biological psychiatry; and suggest conceptual and resource requirements for further development in this area.

CONVERGENCE OF HEALTH AND BEHAVIOR

Within the past decade, politically inspired interest in three distinct domains—health promotion and disease prevention, clinical care, and research—has underscored the need for a major reconceptualization and expansion of research at the interface of medicine and behavior. With respect to health promotion and disease prevention, two political documents issued in the 1970s formally sanctioned the concept that behavior is a legitimate focus for action in health care. In 1974, the Lalonde Report (3) from Canada noted emphatically the role of behavioral and lifestyle factors in the development of disease and recommended strengthened preventive efforts. This theme was elaborated in 1979 by the U.S. Surgeon General's report *Healthy People* (4). Both documents emphasized early preventive efforts aimed at changing health-relevant behaviors; neither addressed needs for basic or clinical research involving people who already manifested symptoms of illness.

In the second domain of activity, clinical care, the growth of psychiatric consultation-liaison programs has been a key development. Consultation-liaison is now an integral part of most psychiatric training and constitutes an important addition to the care of the medically ill. Not only does the application of Engel's "biopsychosocial model" (5) make good clinical sense, but recent evidence also suggests that the integration of mental health care into general health care can reduce the overall costs of medical care (6–8).

More recently, a number of developments in research have focused attention on the interaction of biological and behavioral variables. The report by the Institute of Medicine on *Health and Behavior: Frontiers of Research in the Biobehavioral Sciences* (9) presented convincing evidence that much of the world's burden of illness is behavior-related; it estimated that in the United States, 50 percent of mortality from the 10 leading causes of death is attributable to such "lifestyle" factors as cigarette smoking, excessive consumption of alcoholic beverages, illicit drug use, certain dietary habits, reckless driving, nonadherence to effective medication regimens, and maladaptive responses to social pressures. The report also described many promising research opportunities at the interface of health and behavior. An increasingly significant element of this broad range of "biobehavioral" research focuses on the relationship between medical and psychiatric conditions. Early studies on stress research and on psychosomatic medicine have been augmented by the expanding knowledge of human physiology and the development of behavioral and social science techniques to assess human experiences. The explosion of information and research technologies in the neurosciences has tremendous potential for observing and understanding the interactions between medical and psychiatric conditions.

PSYCHIATRIC AND MEDICAL CONDITIONS: MODELS OF INTERACTION

Psychiatric and medical conditions can interrelate with one another in a variety of ways. Figure 1 depicts four conceptual models of interrelationships. These models are not mutually exclusive; depending upon the amount of information known or the question to be addressed, these relationships can be considered in more than one way.

Co-occurrent Conditions

The co-occurent model (Figure 1A) assumes that psychiatric and medical conditions exist simultaneously and independently in the same patient without a putative etiopathogenetic link. Examples of co-occurrent conditions include the schizophrenic patient who has a myocardial infarction or the depressed patient with lymphoma. Typically, interactions exist that will affect the course of both disorders: for example, the schizophrenic patient

Co-occurrent

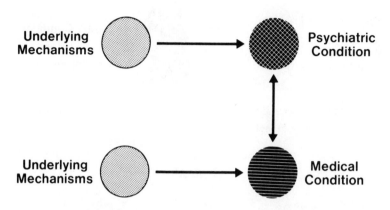

Figure 1A. Model of interaction of psychiatric and medical conditions: co-occurrent conditions.

Linked Occurrence

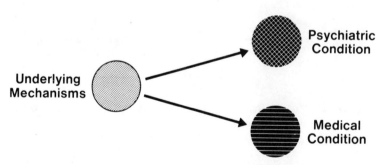

Figure 1B. Model of interaction of psychiatric and medical conditions: conditions with linked occurrence.

may experience difficulty in communicating his symptoms of angina, leading the physician to think that they are paranoid delusional symptoms instead; in the second example, the affectively ill patient may find that symptoms stemming from chemotherapy for lymphoma exacerbate his depressed state.

Common Symptomatology

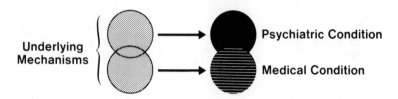

Figure 1C. Model of interaction of psychiatric and medical conditions: conditions with common symptomatology.

Causal

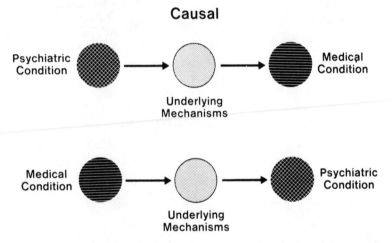

Figure 1D. Model of interaction of psychiatric and medical conditions: conditions with causal linkage.

Linked Occurrence of Conditions

As more information becomes available, one may find that the co-occurrence of two disorders is more prevalent than expected. Although there is no apparent causal relationship between the two disorders, it is possible that there is a link to a common diathesis (Figure 1B). For example, National Institutes of Health (NIH) physicians have observed clinically that a significant number of people with Type V hyperlipoproteinemia manifest behavioral symptoms similar to those found in patients with somatization disorder (J. Hoeg, personal communication). Fras et al. (10) have reported higher-than-expected associations between endogenomorphic depression and undiagnosed carcinoma of the pancreas. In each case the underlying pathophysiologic mechanisms that might account for the link need to be examined. As information about the relationship accumulates, one could begin to explore hypotheses about potential causal connections.

Conditions With Common Symptomatology

Many psychiatric syndromes are constituted by symptoms that, in the context of a primary medical disorder, probably would not be viewed as psychiatric symptoms. In this model (Figure 1C), it becomes apparent that both disorders have a common subset of symptoms or signs; these need not be present in all patients, nor will the patient in any given case necessarily be thought of as having psychiatric symptoms per se. For example, some symptoms associated with panic disorder—most notably, palpitations and dyspnea—are also seen in patients with mitral valve prolapse or other hyperdynamic cardiac conditions (11). Research focusing on these relationships may lead to explanations of the development of these symptomatic states.

Causal Links Between Conditions

In the causal model, interactions between psychiatric and medical conditions (Figure 1D) occur in either of two ways. A pre-existing psychiatric disorder or behavioral state can affect the development or onset of medical disorder; an example is the association of bereavement with risk for disease, particularly in men (12). Alternatively, a pre-existing medical disorder can affect the development or onset of psychiatric disorder. For example, patients with CNS sarcoidosis may manifest neurological, cognitive, and affective symptoms (13), or patients with Cushing's syndrome may develop symptoms of a major depressive disorder (14).

In each case, the relationships can be either *primary*, where a direct linkage exists between the two states, or *secondary*, where the relationship is a function of the treatment or of adaptive mechanisms associated with the psychological state. For example, administration of exogenous corticosteroids to treat autoimmune disorders could produce a depression similar to that of Cushing's syndrome.

MECHANISMS OF INTERACTION

Underlying the various interrelationships of medical and psychiatric conditions are a set of mediating mechanisms depicted in Figure 2. This generic model considers the presence of both a medical condition and a behavioral or psychiatric condition and indicates the range of possible interactions as mediated by: a) physiologic mechanisms; b) behavioral adaptive mechanisms; and c) the treatment process itself.

Physiologic mechanisms are well expressed in Weiner's (15) notion of the brain as a transducer of human experience into physiologic changes. More specifically, these mediators consist of the full range of neuroregulatory, endocrinologic, cardiovascular, and immunologic mechanisms which affect end-organ system. Of prime importance are the neurochemical processes described in the introductory chapter; they are of central interest to neuroscientists and are becoming increasingly researchable through the growing armamentarium of the neurosciences.

Medical and psychiatric conditions also interact through the mediation of behavioral or adaptive mechanisms. These include, for example, the absence or dysfunction of social support systems, coping strategies, and other health-relevant behaviors that develop in response to these conditions. These mediating mechanisms are affected by personal or constitutional capacities (intelligence, temperament, and so forth), sociodemographic status (age, socioeconomic status, and so forth), and sociocultural content (occupation, ethnic background). These mechanisms are modified by experience through interaction with the physiologic mediators, and through interaction with the conditions themselves.

Clinical interventions involved in both the diagnosis and treatment of illness are a third mediating mechanism. These interventions, whether pharmacologic or psychosocial, can exert their effects either intentionally or unintentionally. Thus, medication or psychotherapy used to treat a psychiatric condition may create or exacerbate a co-occurrent medical condition. For example, lithium carbonate may cause the development of a hypothyroid state in a patient with bipolar affective disorder. Conversely, psychotherapy may contribute to the improvement of a co-occurrent medical condition. For example, for a patient with dysthymia, cognitive-behavioral therapy may improve his sense of self-efficacy and thereby increase compliance with his medical regimen for the treatment of co-occurrent cardiovascular disease.

Consideration of a disorder such as acquired immune deficiency syndrome (AIDS) illustrates an application of the generic model (16). The basic pathophysiology of the disorder, the incapacitation of the body's immune system, results in manifest medical symp-

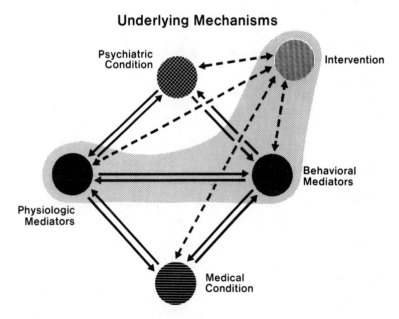

Underlying Mechanisms

Figure 2. Mechanisms of interaction of psychiatric and medical conditions.

toms as a result of opportunistic infections and neoplastic disease. Growing evidence indicates that an important direct effect of the disease is the development of significant cognitive and affective symptoms, presumably through an encephalitic process (17). Significant depressive and stress-related symptoms often occur at the same time, both as a reaction to the disease process and to the concomitant social isolation. These symptoms conceivably could further reduce T-cell functioning, thereby affecting the course of the illness itself. In addition, drugs used in the treatment of the disease—for example, interferon in high doses—could result in or exacerbate psychiatric symptoms (Renault et al, unpublished manuscript, 1983). It is significant that all of these interactions are superimposed on a disease in which the nature of transmission is strongly influenced by behavioral factors.

RESEARCH QUESTIONS AND OPPORTUNITIES

This conceptual approach to the integration of psychiatric and medical disorders raises numerous research questions that require

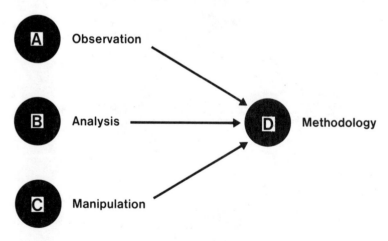

Figure 3. Research questions useful in elucidating the nature and mode of interaction between medical and psychiatric conditions.

techniques and strategies suggested by developments in neuroscience. Figure 3 portrays four categories of research questions. The first category consists of *observational* or *descriptive* questions, which attempt to address the nature and extent of the apparent or putative relationship between given medical and psychiatric conditions. Attempts to answer these questions might require cross-sectional or time-course studies with either the medical or the psychiatric condition serving as the independent or as the dependent variable. A second category of *analytic* questions seeks to examine the underlying or mediating mechanisms that might elucidate etiologic and pathogenetic factors. The neuroscientific strategies and tools described in the first chapter are most applicable to such questions. *Manipulative* or *evaluative* questions involve manipulating diagnostic or treatment-related variables; research designed to address these issues typically uses measures of suspected underlying mechanisms or of symptomatic states as dependent variables. Needs for the development or refinement of research assessment, measurement, and design techniques are addressed through the use of a fourth category—*methodologic* questions, which are related to each of the other categories.

APPLICATIONS OF THE INTEGRATED MODEL

This section will suggest possible applications of the research questions and interactive models of medical and psychiatric conditions previously discussed.

Co-occurrent Disorders: Lymphoma and Depression

While the co-occurrence of these disorders has been noted anecdotally, little evidence regarding the frequency or the nature of this co-occurrence exists.

Observational-descriptive questions offer a means of obtaining evidence: Is the co-occurrence of depression and lymphoma great enough to suggest a linked occurrence? Does the co-occurrence of these disorders influence their course or outcome?

Attempts to answer these two questions involve, in turn, a methodologic question: How does one diagnose depression in the context of a medical illness that produces the same vegetative disturbances as seen in depression?

The co-occurrence of the two conditions also suggests an analytic question: Does depression or its physiologic concomitants have an impact on or further perturb immunoregulatory disturbances in lymphoma?

The implications of a positive response to this question suggest the need for another methodologic query: What are the relevant immunologic measures that may best reveal the impact, if any, of depression on lymphoma?

Finally, interest in the co-occurrence of lymphoma and depression suggests two manipulative-evaluative questions pertaining to clinical research: How does treatment or absence of treatment of co-occurrent depression influence the course of lymphoma? What impact do therapeutic modalities selected for treatment of lymphoma have on the depression?

The issues raised by these two questions suggest a new methodologic requirement: the need to select outcome measures that will assess the efficacy of treatment for depression in the context of a co-occurrent medical disorder.

Linked Occurrence: Type V Hyperlipoproteinemia and Somatization Disorders

A similar research approach can be developed for an example of the linked occurrence of psychiatric and medical conditions. Observational-descriptive questions offer a means of determining the validity and generalizability of observations and the need for further research: Is there an increased frequency of somatization disorder in patients with type V hyperlipoproteinemia? If so, is the excess of somatization disorder limited to or linked exclusively to type V hyperlipoproteinemia?

Specifying observational-descriptive research questions suggests the need to first address a methodologic consideration: Are the

DSM-III criteria for somatization disorder sufficient to describe the behavioral abnormalities observed empirically?

If so, an analytic question follows: Are the behavioral abnormalities attributable to a direct central or peripheral effect of the lipoprotein disturbance, or are both conditions related to some common underlying mechanism?

A related methodologic issue also must be addressed: Do peripheral lipoprotein measures reflect the central milieu?

Finally, a manipulative-evaluative question and a related methodologic question can be asked: Does dietary or pharmacologic reversal of the lipoprotein abnormality influence the behavioral abnormality? How does one measure change in the behavioral disturbance?

Issues concerning the relationship between the depression-like symptoms of bereavement and the development of physical disease are of particular interest and warrant brief discussion. The Institute of Medicine (12) recently reported research evidence linking the death of a spouse with excess medical and psychiatric morbidity, an increase in health-damaging behaviors, such as alcohol abuse and smoking, and, for widowed men under 75 years of age, an increased risk of mortality for several years. Although data associating bereavement with specific diseases are limited, it has been suggested that there is an association with cardiovascular disease, vulnerability to certain infectious diseases, depression, suicide, and accidents. Studies designed to answer additional observational questions are likely to elucidate still other associations in this area.

Numerous studies in both animals and man have examined neuroregulatory and other physiologic mechanisms to determine if they can mediate the effects of bereavement (12). Given the association between bereavement and cardiovascular disorders, more studies are needed to focus on the role of the autonomic nervous system as a mediator between stressful events and vulnerability to cardiac ventricular rhythm disturbances (18). Another area of active investigation is the neuroendocrinology of stress, described recently in detail by Axelrod and Reisine (19).

The dramatic expansion of both neurobiological variables and

immunologic measures makes the relatively new field of "psycho-
neuroimmunology" an important area for examining analytic
questions. Recent evidence, for example, suggests changes in in
vitro measures of T-cell function in widowers following the death
of their wives (20). While it is still unclear whether or not such
measures of immune function are clinically significant, the approach represents a powerful means of studying mind-body relationships.

CONSULTATION-LIAISON RESEARCH AT NIMH/NIH

The Consultation-Liaison Service of the NIMH Intramural Program has initiated the Biobehavioral Research Program, which is
dedicated to the exploration of the interface between medicine
and psychiatry and utilizes many of the concepts discussed in this
chapter (21). For example, a study of Cushing's syndrome was
designed not only to answer descriptive questions about the incidence of affective disturbances in patients with this disorder but
also to answer analytic questions about the relationship between
the degree of cortisol production and cognitive deficits (in order to
test a similar relationship observed in patients with affective disorder (22)) and to establish disorder-specific response patterns to CRF
(23). Manipulative-evaluative questions about the efficacy of cortisol blocking agents, such as metyrapone and customary psychotropic agents, in the treatment of affective symptoms related to
Cushing's syndrome are also being addressed.

Another ongoing project at the NIH/NIMH Clinical Center is a
prospective study of the development of psychiatric syndromes in
patients taking steroids. This investigation involves the following
questions: *descriptive* questions (what percentage of patients receiving steroids develop psychiatric complications, and how does
prior history of psychiatric illness influence the likelihood of
developing steroid-related psychiatric complications?); *analytic*
questions (do peripheral biochemical markers, such as dopamine-
HVA, that appear related to steroid administration in vitro (24) and
to psychosis in vivo (25) predict development of untoward steroid
reactions?); and *manipulative-evaluative* questions (what psycho-

tropic agents may be best employed to treat steroid-related psychiatric disorders?).

The longitudinal, multiaxial design of these and other studies being conducted through the Consultation-Liaison Service of the NIMH Intramural Research Program allows for hypothesis-generating activity as well as hypothesis testing through the integration of modern neuroscience techniques into interface research. Other studies currently under way at the Clinical Center include 10 research protocols involving six different Institutes. These studies are investigating the cognitive, behavioral, and affective concomitants of cancer of the pancreas, AIDS, thyroid replacement and withdrawal, interferon therapy for chronic active hepatitis, metoclopramide administration, and other topics.

CONCLUSIONS

While the availability of new technologies and procedures and the development of significant research questions are necessary for the advancement of the field, they are not sufficient. There must be a general conceptual reorientation at the broader institutional level. Most significant is the need for sufficient additional funding for more research at the interface of psychiatry and general medicine. This kind of research often falls through the cracks of academic departments and NIH and ADAMHA Institutes. Second, research training programs need to train people to engage specifically in clinical investigations related to this interface. This should include training in both specific research techniques and in understanding the clinical problems of patients with medical and psychiatric conditions. Both biological psychiatric research and consultation-liaison psychiatry must shift their frame of reference to include each others domains.

Consultation-liaison psychiatry flowered under federal support for clinical training that did not require any research involvement; it now finds itself preoccupied with generating money for clinical services and teaching activities and, thus, still devotes little time to research. The development of an active research component that would include significant interaction with the neurosciences should be a top priority for consultation-liaison psychiatry. Such efforts would strengthen the research foundations of both psychiatry and medicine. Moreover, the application of biomedical research paradigms in medical settings could improve the awareness of our general medical colleagues about psychiatric conditions in their patients, enhance the acceptance of psychiatric concepts, and, ultimately, improve the care and quality of life of patients.

References

1. President's Commission on Mental Health: Report to the President. Washington, DC, US Government Printing Office, 1978

2. Institute of Medicine: Research on Stress and Human Health: Report of a Study. Washington, DC, National Academy Press, 1981

3. Lalonde M: A new perspective on the health of Canadians: a working document. Ottawa, Information Canada, 1974

4. Office of the Assistant Secretary for Health and Surgeon General: Healthy people: the Surgeon General's report on health promotion and disease prevention. Washington, DC, US Government Printing Office, 1979

5. Engel GL: The need for a new medical model: a challenge for biomedicine. Science 196:129–135, 1977

6. Jones KR, Vischi TR: Impact of alcohol, drug abuse, and mental health treatment on medical care utilization: a review of the research literature. Med Care 17(Suppl):1–82, 1979

7. Levitan SJ, Kornfeld DS: Clinical and cost benefits of liaison psychiatry. Am J Psychiatry 138:790–793, 1981

8. Mumford E, Schlesinger HJ, Glass GV, et al.: A new look at evidence about reduced costs of medical utilization following mental health treatment. Am J Psychiatry 141:1145–1159, 1984

9. Institute of Medicine: Health and Behavior: Frontiers of Research in the Biobehavioral Sciences. Washington, DC, National Academy Press, 1982

10. Fras I, Litin EM, Pearson JS: Comparison of psychiatric symptoms in carcinoma of the pancreas with those and some other intra-abdominal neoplasms. Am J Psychiatry 123:1553–1561, 1967

11. Jefferson JW, Marshall JR: Cardiovascular disorders, in Neuropsychiatric Features of Medical Disorders. New York, Plenum Publishing Corp, 1981

12. Institute of Medicine: Bereavement: Reactions, Consequences, and Care. Washington, DC, National Academy Press, 1984

13. Stoudemire A, Linfors E, Houpt J, et al.: Central nervous system sarcoidosis. Gen Hosp Psychiatry 5:129–132, 1983

14. Starkman MN, Schteingart DE, Schork MA: Depressed mood and other psychiatric manifestations of Cushing's syndrome: relationship to hormone levels. Psychosom Med 43:3–18, 1981

15. Weiner H: Psychobiology and Human Disease. New York, Elsevier, 1977

16. Nichols SE, Ostrow DG: Psychiatric Implications of Acquired Immune Deficiency Syndrome. Washington, DC, American Psychiatric Press, 1984

17. Britton CB: Neurology of acquired immune deficiency syndrome, in Psychiatric Implications of Acquired Immune Deficiency Syndrome. Edited by Nichols SE, Ostrow DG. Washington, DC, American Psychiatric Press, 1984

18. Verrier RL, Lown B: Autonomic nervous system and malignant cardiac arrhythmias, in Brain, Behavior, and Bodily Disease. Edited by Weiner H, Hofer MA, Stunkard AJ. New York, Raven Press, 1981

19. Axelrod J, Reisine TD: Stress hormones: their interaction and regulation. Science 224:452–460, 1984

20. Schleifer SJ, Keller SE, Camerino M, et al.: Suppression of lympho-cyte stimulation following bereavement. JAMA 250:374–399, 1983

22. Rubinow DR, Post RM, Savard R, et al.: Cortisol hypersecretion and cognitive impairment in depression. Arch Gen Psychiatry 41:279–283, 1984

21. Rubinow DR: Research strategies at the interface of medicine and psychiatry. Gen Hosp Psychiatry 5:99–103, 1983

22. Rubinow DR, Post RM, Savard R, et al.: Cortisol hypersecretion and cognitive impairment in depression. Arch Gen Psychiatry 41:279–283, 1984

23. Gold PW, Chrousos GP, Kellner C, et al.: Psychiatric implications of basic and clinical studies with corticotropin releasing factor. Am J Psychiatry 141:619–628, 1984

24. Rothschild AJ, Schatzberg AF, Langlais PJ, et al.: Dexamethasone elevates dopamine in human plasma and rat brain, in Abstracts of the Annual Meeting of the American College of Neuropsychophar-macology, December 12–16, 1983

25. Pickar D, Labarca R, Linnoila M, et al.: Neuroleptic-induced decrease in plasma homovanillic antipsychotic activity in schizophrenic pa-tients. Science 225:954–957, 1984